IF YOU OWN A HORSE—
IF YOU PLAN TO BUY ONE—
OR IF YOU JUST LOVE HORSES

. . . here's a valuable guide on how to select one, care for it, feed it, safeguard its health —even breed it, if you plan to go into horse raising seriously.

Written by a specialist in the field, this common-sense book contains the information you need to give your horse the finest care he can get . . . and to enjoy him at his best.

TOP FORM® BOOK OF
HORSE CARE

By FREDERICK HARPER

POPULAR LIBRARY · NEW YORK

POPULAR LIBRARY EDITION

DEDICATION

This book is dedicated to the memory of my grandparents: Isabel France, writer, and Owen France, horseman.

PREFACE

The problems and questions of the present-day horse owner and breeder with regard to the care of his horses are my daily concern. Being an owner-breeder myself helps bring into greater reality and sharper focus the situation of the owners and breeders. Never before in the history of this great country has the horse had such an impact on our economy and society. The importance of the horse as a source of pleasure and sport is best illustrated by the tremendous growth in the number of boys and girls enrolled in the 4-H Horse Project in the United States, which increased from 37,531 in 1959 to 224,540 in 1969.

Tough competition on the racetrack, in the show ring and on the trail, and the pride of ownership, send the horse owner in a search for factual information that will help him provide his horse with the best possible care and at the same time give him a greater opportunity to win.

Modern horse owners are not satisfied simply to be told *how* to do something. They want to know *why* it should be done. It has been my experience that a more efficient job will be accomplished when a person understands why it is necessary to groom a horse daily, feed him a balanced ration, worm him periodically, etc. Throughout this book an attempt has been made to include the scientific *whys* along with the practical *hows*.

In following this practice, this book is not intended as a do-it-yourself veterinary guide. Horses are too valuable as animals and precious as friends to be without trained professional assistance when it is needed. Call your veterinarian when your horse has a disease or an injury.

7

I want to express my sincere appreciation to William Laas for his editorial aid; to Orren Mixer, whose talent and knowledge of horses resulted in the beautiful cover of this book; and to Dom Lupo for his detailed illustrations.

I am indebted to Dr. S. P. Dey, equine practitioner of Allentown, New Jersey, for reviewing Chapters 6, 12, 13, 14 and 15; and to my colleagues, Dr. Paul Fonnesbeck, Assistant Professor of Nutrition, for reviewing Chapters 9, 10 and 11; Dr. James G. Welch, Associate Professor of Nutrition, for reviewing Chapter 16.

To my wife, Brenda, goes my deepest gratitude for her invaluable assistance in the preparation of the entire manuscript and for her continual encouragement and inspiration.

Lastly, I want to recognize the thousands of horse owners and horse lovers without whom this book would not be needed.

Frederick Harper
Extension Associate in Horse Management
Rutgers—The State University
New Brunswick, New Jersey

FOREWORD

The resurgence of the horse in American society today makes a book such as this a most welcome aid to all horse owners. It will benefit thousands of horsemen, and horses as well.

It has been said that in recent years the equine industry has become the nation's No. 1 pleasure industry from the standpoint of people and dollars involved, both in active and spectator participation. Increasing interest in equine medicine is just one indication that this is true.

The American Association of Equine Practitioners, a group of veterinarians specializing in equine practice, was formed about ten years ago when the pleasure horse industry was beginning to stir. (There had been little demand for equine practitioners before.) In the early years of the Association there were fewer than a hundred members. Today there are 2,000 veterinarians who engage full or part time in equine practice.

Significantly, almost $1,000,000 will be spent on research in equine disease problems during the coming year; until five years ago the total spent on equine research had for many years been less than $50,000 annually.

Another indicator of the growing interest in horses is the amazing enthusiasm of the nation's youngsters for equine sports and activities. Approximately a quarter million youngsters are involved in organized 4-H, Future Farmers of America, and Boy Scout horse projects this year, reflecting a three-fold increase in the past five years. Probably an even greater number are engaged in unorganized equine sports and recreational activities.

The vast nationwide network of horse shows, rodeos, riding clubs and horse centers has come into being only recently. Polo and racing have been revived and greatly expanded. Thoroughbreds, Standardbreds and Quarter Horses now race on hundreds of tracks in all parts of the country. There is hardly a city or town where one cannot attend or participate in some sort of entertaining equine sports event almost any weekend of the year.

And yet, many think of the heyday of the horse as being in the early 1900's, when there were 26,000,000 horses and mules in the United States. However, they were largely draft animals bred and maintained as horsepower for farming and transport. By today's standards, not many were good pleasure horses.

But, over the years, owners of purebred horses of the many American breeds, as well as the imported breeds, organized into breed associations, each improving and promoting its chosen breed. The number of registered purebred horses of all breeds today far exceeds that at any other time in history. The quality of the horse population has also improved, and it is probable that the net value of the current horse population more than exceeds that of the 26,000,000 of fifty years ago.

This may be a surprising comparison, but just as surprising is the level of horsemanship and horse management practiced in the so-called heyday of the horse. During the Civil War the average service life for a cavalry horse was *less than five months*. Poor management and lack of disease control, and the absence of veterinary service or training schools for horse management, were all to blame.

There was no improvement until late in World War I, when the American fighting forces on the Western Front in Europe were practically immobilized for lack of horses. Neglect, poor management and disease were taking such a heavy toll of American horses that the French government refused to deliver 80,000 replacement horses to the American Army because it was obvious that they would be wasted. This fiasco resulted in the establishment of the Army Veterinary Corps and the U.S. Cavalry School, where horse management was intensively taught.

The establishment of a serious, forward-looking horse program by the Army resulted in training programs that produced thousands of knowledgeable horsemen. Most important, it resulted in the publication of numerous training manuals and facts on horse care and management.

Although the horse program faded from the Army twenty-five years ago, the knowledge gained was recorded and carries on. It was, in fact, the forerunner of a vast array of books and magazines that have been published in recent years. Today's new horse owner no longer needs to depend on opinionated and distorted word-of-mouth instructions for guidance. He may easily obtain literally dozens of interesting publications on horses.

Horse owners of this generation are mostly new owners who had little or no contact with or knowledge of horses a few years ago. With the horse now firmly established as a companion and pleasure animal, this influx of new, unsophisticated owners will continue. But, with the information now readily available to them, they need not and generally do not remain unsophisticated for long. Many modern advances make owning a horse today a real pleasure rather than a chore; modern design in stables and equipment of every sort contribute to the comfort and convenience of both horse and rider.

Into such an atmosphere, this new book, *Top Form Book of Horse Care*, is most welcome as an additional source of information. New owners will especially enjoy it. All who read it will benefit; but, most of all, the horse will benefit. What a pity this and other books like it were not available when so badly needed by him a half century ago!

Wayne O. Kester, D.V.M.
Brig. Gen. USAF (VC) Ret.

CONTENTS

Chapter 1

Horses for Fun

Man's ancient and honored friend, the horse, has never been as popular as he is in the United States today. Horsemanship, including both the riding and care of these beautiful and lovable animals, is one of the fastest growing of all pleasure and sport activities. The horse has made a dramatic comeback at the very time that mechanical horsepower has taken over most of the work he used to do.

As a companion to man, horses for thousands of years have symbolized strength, courage, and nobility. It is perhaps because of this that many patriotic paintings and statues portray leaders and heroes mounted. A horse with flowing mane and tail gives a majestic appearance; and the man, woman, boy, or girl astride a horse feels a reflection of traditional glory.

Today the horse is less important to our workaday life as a source of transportation and farm power than in the past. Just before World War I, the number of farm horses in America reached a peak of 26 million. By 1959 the number of horses and mules had declined to about 3 million. But today we own more pleasure horses than in the pre-motor age when work animals plowed every farmer's fields and clopped down every city street.

What is the reason for the rediscovery of the horse? The need for recreation is no doubt one reason and the fun and exercise of riding, or exhibiting one's animal in a show, are others. Another is the character and personality of an animal that has never been far from man's side through the centuries. The beauty, speed, ability, and friendliness of a horse exude a magnetism that draws people of all ages.

Except in ranching and other specialized jobs that require horses—cars, trucks, and tractors furnish the muscle for transportation and agriculture today. This fact has contributed to the pleasure horse boom of the past ten years. Thanks to cars, more people move from city to suburb where they can find convenient open space for maintaining an animal. With more leisure at their disposal, they can also find the time. We seem to be learning that the tensions and pressures of the Motor Age can be put aside, forgotten, and rendered harmless on the back of a horse.

A rising percentage of all horses are pleasure horses and the animals are owned by individuals, rather than by professional breeders of livestock. In New Jersey, in 1961, the average horse owner owned a total of 3.5 animals with 1.7 acres of pasture per horse—neither a large herd nor a large amount of land. In New York, the enthusiasm of individual owners has built the head count to approximately 125,000, with annual expenditures of $200 million for goods and services.

These statistics from populous states are most revealing. In California, where one would naturally expect to find many horses, there are 310,000 head and an industry worth $165 million annually. A New York study shows a spread of ownership over a broad range of income levels; owning a horse is now the pleasure of many suburban families. Horseback riding is so popular a recreation that the average American over twelve years of age may be expected to do more than a day's riding each year.

Horsemanship offers a way of getting back to nature in the truest sense. One deals with a living creature, not a machine. Huge crowds watch, fascinated, as horses are raced and exhibited every day and on many evenings under the lights. Rodeos and circus performances by trained animals attract great audiences, too. Cowboys still ride the Western range, and in some parts of our country—especially Maryland, New Jersey and Virginia—the fox hunter canters across hill and dale. Whether in war or on peaceful expeditions, when the going gets too rough for gasoline vehicles, soldiers and explorers still turn to the sure-footed horse or his relatives, the mule, the pony, or the burro.

Few American children, however, enjoy the opportunity farm children once had, that of growing up with horses as part of their everyday life.

Country boys and girls used to learn at an early age how to mount and ride, how to drive a team, how to feed a horse, or how to come to the aid of a mare at foaling time. Today they may learn to drive a car before ever having entered a barn or a stable. The technique of how to act properly around a horse should be developed gradually.

To enjoy your horse to the fullest, you need to provide good care for the sake of his health and good management for the sake of your pocketbook. A horse represents a good-sized investment that will pay only if your horse remains healthy and dependable. Because there are many old-fashioned misconceptions about horses, this book is being written to give you essential, up-to-date information on all aspects of care and management—from feeding to breeding. If you own or intend to own a horse, you would do well to acquire a bit of horse know-how.

You could also enjoy and learn more about horses by joining one of the thousands of local horse groups and taking part in its activities. Most counties in the United States have at least a riding club. Here is how you might go about finding them: If you are interested in a particular breed, write to its national association. (See pages 36-39 for names and addresses.) Most of them have state or regional affiliates. Your county agriculture agent can help you find a group of horse lovers and can provide you with educational material and assistance as well.

The local organizations sponsor shows, trail rides, gymkhanas, judging contests, and educational activities such as clinics. The sport of showing horses has grown tremendously. The American Horse Show Association, 527 Madison Ave., New York, N.Y. 10022, recognizes several hundred shows annually in various divisions, for example:

Appaloosa	Junior Hunter and	Quarter Horse
Arabian	Jumper	Roadster
Dressage	Morgan	Saddle Horse
Equitation	Palomino	Shetland Pony
Hackney	Parade	Tennessee Walking
Harness Pony	Pinto	Horse
Hunter	Polo Pony	Welsh Pony
Hunter and	Pony of the	Western
Jumper Pony	Americas	
Jumper		

These names designate either a breed of horse (Appaloosa, Arabian) or a type of show performance (Dressage, Hunter).

In addition, breed association shows are particularly numerous. For example, the American Quarter Horse Association approved 1,543 shows for that breed in 1969, most of which had youth activity classes. Thousands more local "weekend" shows take place every year not approved by any association.

The list also reveals that many classes are for "juniors." Horsemanship programs for youth have had a fabulous growth. The largest is the 4-H Horse Project. It has grown from 37, 531 members in 1959 to more than 224,000 in 1969.

Organized by the Cooperative Extension Service of the U.S. Department of Agriculture, 4-H Clubs offer fun and fellowship to boys and girls aged nine to nineteen, and they help improve their knowledge, skills, and character as well. The 4-H Horse Project is nationally sponsored by Merck & Co., Inc., Rahway, New Jersey. You can learn how it functions from your state 4-H leader or county 4-H extension agent. Although the 4-H Club activity was started on our farms, it is growing fastest today in the suburbs of large metropolitan areas.

Horses have been one of mankind's most dependable allies since prehistoric times. Companionship with a horse can be one of the most enjoyable, rewarding experiences of your life. All it takes is understanding. As an aid to understanding, let's begin by answering a simple question: What makes a horse a horse? We shall see in Chapter 2.

The Horse as Companion to Man

You see a picture from Greek mythology of a centaur, half man, half horse. You smile. "How kooky," you say. "There's no such animal!" But hold on a moment. In a way, perhaps, centaurs did exist. The ancient Greek image gives proof that men and horses were companions thousands of years before recorded history began.

The original "Centaurs" were a primitive mountain tribe who lived in the north of Greece, long before the birth of Christ. They worshipped the horse, considering him sacred to the moon. Like our own Hopi Indians, these people performed rain dances. While prancing around on gaudily decorated hobbyhorses, they appealed to the moon to make it rain. In sculpturing a horse with the head and torso of a man, the later, more civilized Greeks left us a vivid impression of these horse dancers in action.

By that time, which seems to us so long ago, the Dawn Horse had already been roaming the earth for 45 to 50 million years. Very few mammals still surviving today can claim such a heritage. To the best of our knowledge, man appeared on earth no earlier than one million years ago.

The long history of *Equus caballus* is a tribute to an amazing ability to adapt to a changing environment. During the course of time, the Ice Age and other cruel changes in climate totally exterminated many less hardy species. We know only by digging up fossilized bones that creatures such as the mastodon and the saber-toothed tiger ever existed at all.

ORIGIN IN AMERICA

Where did the horse originate? Right here in North America! This is a surprising fact because when Columbus

discovered America in 1492, there was not a horse to
be found. The Indians had never seen one. Yet skeletons of
Eohippus, the Dawn Horse, which you can see in museums
were dug up on our Western plains.

Eohippus was a little animal about 12 inches high—not
much larger than a fox. He had four toes and a splint on his
forefeet and three toes and a splint on his hindfeet. One toe
on each foot was larger than the others and he could run extremely fast. And run *Eohippus* did for millions of years.

It is easy to understand why those animals of the species
who could run the fastest and wander the farthest in search
of food had the best chance of survival. With each generation, by natural selection, the descendants of *Eohippus*
developed legs a little longer, lungs a little bigger for good
wind and stamina, and stronger teeth for chewing tough wild
grasses—or maybe even for biting an enemy.

He gradually grew taller and larger. Also only one toe
touched the ground; this allowed for greater speed. Even-
tually the second and fourth toes became the splint bones.
What happened to the first and fifth toes, no one knows.
They just disappeared with time. By the time of the last Ice
Age, about one million years ago, all four feet had hooves.
Hippus had grown to the size of a small pony—*Equus*, the
common ancestor of every breed of horse we know today.

HE WANDERS THE WORLD

Sometime between the eras of *Eohippus* and of *Equus*, the
prehistoric horses in America wandered up to Alaska. They
crossed the Bering Strait, either on the Arctic ice or via a
land bridge that then existed. They entered the continent of
Asia and found its grasses good. From there the horses
ranged into Europe and Africa—to every part of every continent except Australia, which probably could not be reached
by land.

Meanwhile the American horses disappeared for some
reason still unknown. So when the Spanish Conquistadores
in the sixteenth century brought the first modern horse to
these shores, they were bringing him back home.

ENTER THE HORSEMAN

Primitive man in the Eastern Hemisphere found herds of
horses all around him. We know this because he painted

EVOLUTION OF THE HORSE

EOHIPPUS

MESOHIPPUS

MERYCHIPPUS

PLIOHIPPUS

MODERN DAY HORSE

pictures of them on the walls of caves. No doubt he hunted the horse for meat and used the hides for clothing. Today in some areas of the world horses are still used as a source of food. Just when some caveman genius learned how to tame a horse and make him the servant of our race, we do not know. The early men were nomads, wandering hunters who left few traces of their dwellings and ways of life. We do know that horses were domesticated at least 4,500 years ago, probably first being kept as pets.

The nomads fought constantly to protect or to expand the tribal grazing lands. The man on horseback had an advantage in height, range, and speed over opponents on foot. He also learned to hitch the horse to a vehicle in order to haul goods and people during the tribe's frequent moves. We know that tribes of Huns in central Asia built their entire existence around herds of horses. They ate the meat only of the older or disabled animals and lived mostly on mare's milk.

It says in the Bible (Exodus 14:23): "And the Egyptians pursued, and went in after them to the midst of the sea, even all Pharaoh's horses, his chariots, and his horsemen." Egyptian knowledge of riding and horse-drawn vehicles dates back to about 1700 B.C.

The first "book" about horses that we know of is a set of five stone tablets engraved about 1400 B.C. by Kikkulis. He was the stablemaster of a Hittite king. The Hittites, a people of Asia Minor, were rivals of the Egyptian and Babylonian empires. Kikkulis explained in great detail how to feed, groom, and exercise horses for best results in sport and warfare. Scholars surmise that the Hittites may have been descended from one of the early "horse peoples" who roamed the Asiatic steppes.

Nomadic tribes skilled in horsemanship often became conquerors, attacking civilized and settled farm communities. History tells us of "The Assyrian" who "came down like the wolf on the fold"; of Attila the Hun, the galloping "Scourge of God" in Medieval Europe; of the rough-riding Tartar hordes of Genghis Khan who conquered Russia, China, and India; and of the desert Arabs on their beautiful steeds who spread the word of Allah in the lands around the Mediterranean Sea.

The first equine sports—chariot races and polo—were war-like in nature. The ancient Greeks were accomplished horsemen by civilized standards. They developed the snaffle bit and the relaxed, "balance seat" manner of riding that is still taught to cavalrymen, mounted police, and aspiring riders. For the Olympic Games, which began in 776 B.C., the Greeks built the first hippodrome. Named for *hippos*, the horse, it was an enclosed racecourse with seats for 100,000 persons.

Alexander the Great, on his fiery stallion Bucephalus, used horse knowledge gained from his father in his conquest of the ancient world. Bucephalus, who died at the age of thirty, was buried with military honors, and Alexander founded a city and named it Bucephala after his beloved horse.

EACH BREED TO ITS PURPOSE

Tracing the history of horses as men put them to use has a bearing upon the nature of the horse you ride today. It shows why there are many different breeds. The first wild horses to be tamed were rather small. In about 1880 a surviving link, "Przewalski's horse," was discovered in a remote region of northern Mongolia. This original wild horse still exists and is the only one known to withstand the strife of time. The Przewalski's horse is about the size of a modern pony, stockily built with an erect mane, no forelock; he is a yellowish color usually with a dark strip down the middle of the back and over the shoulder.

Obviously this single type of animal did not suit all of man's needs equally well. Gradually the horse peoples learned that by mating selected animals, they could increase the frequency of certain characteristics in the offspring. (See Chapters 15 and 16 for a discussion of breeding.) But the art of breeding goes way back, in war and in peace.

The Assyrians, for instance, were great warriors and hunters; they trained their horses to answer to pressure of the rider's knees. The hunter or warrior could then have both hands free to hold and shoot his bow and arrow. Our American Indians learned the same trick many centuries later.

The Romans, on the other hand, did not do much riding. In war, their massed heavy infantry, the Roman legion, did very well. The Romans substituted foot-slogging organization and discipline for the swift cavalry thrusts of barbarian warfare. Romans used their horses to pull vehicles along the fine roads they built to the ends of the Empire, and for chariot racing and parades. This called for a stronger, more patient animal than the light horses of the nomads.

In the age of chivalry, the knights in their heavy suits of armor needed a powerful charger to carry the great weight. The horse had to stand like a rock when struck full tilt by the lance of an onrushing foe. He needed intelligence, too, to respond instantly to the signals of his embattled rider. The horse learned complicated maneuvers, such as the pirouette. This manuever survives today in the riding art called dressage.

The knight's steed was necessarily slow of foot. In a charge he needed time to pick up speed, like a car shifting gears from low to high. He went through the natural series of gaits, from walk to trot to full gallop. The Great Horse of chivalry was the ancestor of draft animals like the 2,000-pound, powerful but placid Percheron.

The decisive Battle of Crécy (1346 A.D.) ended the reign of the horse in armor and put him on the farm. The English archers with their longbows shot down the French knights. In England the Norman conquerors had learned to use strong horses in place of oxen to plow their fields. The new source of animal power to replace human labor would dominate the world's agriculture for the next several hundred years.

HORSES IN AMERICA

The horses that the Spaniards brought with them to America frightened the Indians and this may have helped to conquer them. In 1519 the war-horses of Hernando Cortez took part in the conquest of Mexico. Twenty years later Fernando de Soto brought horses into what is now the United States, in the lower Mississippi River region. Some either escaped, were stolen or were traded to the Indians because these horses are the ancestors of the wild mustang herds on the plains. (There are some still running wild.) There has been no native American *hippus* since prehistoric times.

These mustangs are a part of the great American saga of the West, so dear to our hearts. The Indians overcame their fears and became expert horsemen. They rode bareback to hunt buffalo and do battle with rival tribes and white settlers. The white man, too, entered the West on horseback or in horse-drawn covered wagons. From the Mexican *vaquero,* or cowboy, he learned to herd cattle on horseback.

During the Civil War light cavalry, used for scouting or for concealing troop movements, figured in every decisive battle. Pickett's charge at Gettysburg, and Sheridan's ride to Winchester (on the Morgan horse Rienzi) to save his army in the Shenandoah Valley, still live in our memories. After the war, many of these tough troopers from both North and South drifted West to work their trade—whether as cowboys, peace officers, or as the gun-toting outlaws of Wild-West legend.

OUR DEBT TO THE HORSE

The word "horsepower" is an indication of our dependence upon the muscle and good nature of man's ancient companion for many generations. James Watt, inventor of the steam engine that ushered in the modern industrial world, wanted to advertise how much work his new gadget could do. Watt figured that the work of a good draft horse was equal to 550 foot-pounds of work per second. If his engine could do the same, it was a "one-horsepower" engine. We use the identical engineering unit to this day to rate the power of our automobiles.

In war and in sport; in farming, ranching, hauling, building; in carrying the mail by Pony Express; in furnishing the power for the first stagecoaches, canal boats, railroads, trolley cars, and freight wagons; the contribution of the horse is written into every page of American history from its earliest days to the present.

You will want to know how the ancestors of your own horse figured in this gallant history, and you will understand him better as you learn the how and why of his special aptitudes and characteristics. (The story of some individual breeds is discussed in Chapter 4.)

Chapter 3

The Nature of the Horse

We own horses because they are useful and beneficial; but we love horses because they are interesting, friendly animals. Each horse has a specific personality. We should always remember that they are individuals and we should study their ways to understand them better. The relationship of person to horse can become very strong, when he gets to know him well. We can appreciate the horse for himself, not just because we ride him.

To a certain extent, all horses act alike by nature and instinct. The mark of a good horseman, it is said, is that he always seems to know what the horse is going to do an instant *before* the horse himself knows. Like the expert driver of a car in traffic, he anticipates what will happen next and so avoids trouble.

The animal's most useful qualities are his size, speed, strength, and instinct. We know that the evolution of the species provided the horse with long legs and great speed to escape his enemies. This instinct for flight in the face of danger remains deeply ingrained. A horse is timid and alert, suspicious of anything strange and can even sleep standing up.

The horse locks his hind legs into place and throws his front legs into a calf-kneed position when he so chooses, supporting his body solely by tendons and ligaments. He can relax in this position and go to sleep, needing no other support. Whenever you approach a horse, always speak to him quietly from a distance to make sure he will be awake when you come near. Sneaking up on a sleeping horse will startle him; obeying his instinct, he will try to run or kick.

Besides speed, the horse has two means of defense—his teeth and his hooves. When frightened or accidentally startled, his instinct causes him to kick with his hind feet and he often runs for safety. Striking with a fore foot or biting are

27

purposeful means of attack. They are two effective means of protection against wild beasts. The bucking you see at a rodeo recalls the wild state when lions or cougars would attack a horse by leaping on his back. He would try desperately to dislodge the beast before its teeth sunk into his neck.

The ears are a good key to the horse's state of mind. They move about constantly, like radar antennae picking up sounds from various directions. In an alert, they are pointed forward. The horse also raises his head as he listens intently for the source of a suspicious sound. When angry or irritated, he lays his ears straight back.

With eyes set wide apart on the side of his head, the horse can see in all directions, except directly behind him. He can see separate objects with each eye at the same time. That is why he sometimes shies away from a piece of paper or similar object until he can get far enough away to focus both eyes and identify it.

The horse does not have the thinking or reasoning powers of a human being; but his instinct is remarkable nevertheless. Mankind through the ages has taken advantage of the horse's ability to be trained by repetition. Through patient training, the horse tends to perform tasks and duties in response to signals.

A horse seems to remember best how to get from one place to another. If you should get lost on a trail or a road that the horse has covered before, you can usually trust him to find the way home. Some have been known to find their way back from distances of twenty miles or more. Older people remember the milkman's horse; while the milkman delivered milk to one customer, the horse drew the wagon by himself and stopped at the next customer's house.

He is punished for disobeying (for example, by a pull on the rein), and rewarded for obeying by a pat on the neck. When the desired sequence of action sinks in, one can proceed to the next step or stage. The natural instinct of the horse obviously accounts for a large part of his ability to be trained through repetition and association.

A good example is the rider's first lesson: you are always told to mount from the left side. The custom of training horses this way dates from ancient warfare. The knight or cavalryman wore a sword on his left, so it was easier for him to swing the unencumbered right leg over the horse's back.

Today most horses are still trained for mounting and dismounting on the left because of this early custom.

Horses probably communicate with one another not only by nickering and neighing, but in other ways too subtle for human beings to detect. When two strange horses come together for the first time, they go through a sizing-up procedure. They circle around each other cautiously. Then they approach and touch noses. With nostrils distended, they sniff and puff as if thinking the whole thing over. They then investigate each other's tail and body with the tip of the nose. A nibble on the crest of the neck cements the friendship. If they dislike one another, a stamping of the feet and squeals of rage signal the dissension.

Horses often do fight but basic to their nature is the herd instinct. The herd is their natural protection against enemies such as wolves and coyotes. Some horses, when placed alone, will not eat much and often become nervous. For this reason an assortment of pets—dogs, cats, goats—are used as companions for race horses.

There is usually a definite order of rank within a herd. The rules seem to be: (1) dark-colored horses (sorrels or chestnuts, bays and browns) almost always appear at or near the top; (2) mares rank higher than geldings; (3) the older the horse, the higher up on the scale, especially with mares; and (4) size counts, with the good, well-built, medium-sized horse tending to move to the top.

Sometimes a gelding or a barren mare will try to play the role of foster parent to a young foal. For this reason a mare should be stabled or placed in a separate pasture at foaling time. This "foal snatching" may become a serious problem resulting in injury to the mare as she fights to protect and retain her young. The maternal instinct is so strong that old mares have been known to "steal" baby calves. Most mares are protective with their foals and usually try to stay between them and people or even other horses. A word of caution— even a gentle, quiet mare may attack you if you approach her foal.

The age of a horse has an important bearing on his training. One year of a horse's life equals about three and a half years of a man's life. (A five-year-old horse corresponds in age to an eighteen-year-old man.) If the horse is ridden or exercised too hard when immature, especially during the first two or three years, he can, and probably will, develop weaknesses of the legs that most likely will result in an unsoundness.

Old horses do not always "act old"; much depends on their history and state of health. A horse's teeth are the only accurate indication of his age. (This will be explained more fully in Chapter 8.) When a horse reaches an advanced age, the point of the withers becomes sharp and high, the back sinks, and deep sockets may appear above the eyes. Gray hairs show up over the eyes and around the muzzle. Many factors determine the length of life of a horse and much depends on the care it receives. It is not uncommon for horses to live well into their twenties.

Study your horse every day to learn his habits. Watch the way he eats and drinks, and how he acts on a ride. He likes company; if you treat him kindly, he would much rather be with you than alone. He may be patient or impatient, lively or slothful, aggressive or gentle—all these are part of his personality. His traits make him all the more interesting as a companion.

SAFETY RULES FOR HORSE OWNERS

The nature of the horse—his strength and his quickness—puts the burden of safety on the owner and rider. Certain simple rules in handling a horse can avoid serious mishaps. Here is a list of ordinary precautions everyone should follow; they are adapted from the New Jersey *4-H Horse Club Handbook for Members*:

1. Never approach a horse directly from the rear. Even in a single stall it is always possible to approach from an oblique angle so the horse can see you.

2. Always speak to a horse before approaching or touching him. Most horses are likely to jump when startled, and many will kick since they may sleep standing up.

3. If the horse balks on the end of the rope, lead him a few steps forward before touching him with your hand.

4. Keep your head in the clear when bridling the horse. He may throw his head or strike to avoid the bridle. Avoid bridling a nervous horse in close quarters.

5. Walk beside the horse when leading, not ahead or behind him. Always turn the horse to the right, and walk around him.

6. Use a long lead strap and both hands when leading. If the horse rears, release the hand near the halter so you can stay on the ground.

7. The horse is stronger than you, so don't try to outpull him. He will usually respond to a quick snap on the lead strap or rope.

8. Never wrap the lead strap, halter shank, or reins around your hand, wrist, or body.

9. Your safety depends on the good condition of the bridle reins, stirrup leathers, and cinch straps. Replace any strap that begins to show wear.

10. When saddling, stand with your feet well back from his side and reach forward.

11. Never mount a horse in a barn, near fences, trees, or overhanging projections. Sidestepping mounts have injured many riders by collision with such obstacles.

12. Adjust the saddle carefully and cinch it tight enough so it will not slip when you mount. Soon after starting the ride, dismount and tighten the saddle girth again because horses often swell up with air when first saddled. A loose girth can result in serious accidents.

13. If your horse is frightened by an obstacle, dismount and lead him past it.

14. Maintain a secure seat and keep your horse under control at all times. Horses are easily frightened by unusual objects and noises. Anticipate these and steady your mount.

15. When a frightened horse attempts to run, turn him in a circle and tighten the circle until he stops.

16. When riding in a group, do not ride too close to the horse ahead of you and be alert for overhead tree branches.

17. Hold your mount to a walk when going up or down hill.

18. Slow down in rough ground, sand, mud, ice, snow, or whenever there is danger of the mount slipping and falling.

19. Avoid paved roads if possible, and slow to a walk when crossing one. If yours is a spirited or young horse, dismount and lead him across the road. (See safety rules that follow.)

20. Know your horse, his temperament, and predictable reactions to circumstances. Control your temper at all times, but let your mount know that you are his firm and kind master.

SAFETY RULES IN TRAFFIC

Avoiding paved roads is the safest way to keep from mixing horses with automobile traffic. Since this is not always possible, a few additional rules should be observed wherever there are cars.

1. Keep to the right. Pedestrians keep to the left, facing traffic, but a horse cannot, as he may be frightened by cars and trucks rushing directly toward him.

2. Ride well off the side of the road, on the shoulder if there is one—as far to the right as you can get without treading on lawns or other private property.

3. Come to a stop at every crossroad, whether there is a "Stop" sign or not; cars may be approaching at high speed. Make sure none is coming from either direction before proceeding. If with a group, post road guards at each side to stop traffic until the group of riders can pass.

4. At a blind corner (one obscured by a high hedge or embankment) cross to the other side of the road in order to see around it, or dismount and lead the horse around.

5. Avoid parked cars. If it is necessary to pass one, don't go too close, and try to keep the horse's hindquarters pointed away from the car to avoid the chance of his hitting or kicking it.

6. Go no faster than a walk on a paved road, for two reasons: First, the pounding on hard surfaces can injure the feet and leg muscles of your horse, even to the point of making him founder. Second, a galloping horse is difficult to control in automobile traffic. You might frighten the drivers!

7. For night riding wear white or light reflective material to alert motorists of your presence.

8. Obey all traffic signals, lights, signs, or policemen just as if you were driving a car.

Chapter 4

Know Your Horse

What is the difference between a horse and the other animals that almost look like him? The genus *Equus caballus* is distinguished from asses and zebras, for example, by horny chestnuts on the inside of the hind leg, by longer hair on the mane and tail, and by shorter ears. The look of a horse is unmistakable when compared with, for instance, his cousin the donkey.

The difference between a horse and a pony is purely one of size. An animal over 58 inches in height is called a horse, and one less than 58 inches is called a pony. Even this is a loose classification, for registered Shetland and Welsh ponies may not exceed 11.2 hands and 14 hands, respectively. We have cow ponies and polo ponies that may be horse-size, and some horses are actually within the pony category or height.

A *breed* is a group of animals having a common origin and many common characteristics that are readily distinguishable and transmittable to successive generations. The *breed character* consists of the characteristics that distinguish the breeds one from another—those that are inherited—while the *breed type* is the ideal type for horses of a particular breed.

Differences in breed character are not unlike differences among races of men: average height, shape of face and body, color of skin and hair, temperament, and physical strength. Most of the breeds originated, as we know, in answer to the special needs of the people who owned them.

A *breeder* is the owner of the dam at the time of service, although the Jockey Club that registers Thoroughbreds denotes a breeder as the owner of the dam at the time of foaling. If one raises foals whose parents are recorded in the same registry association the animals are then called purebreds and the foals may be registered with the same breed association.

Notice that the word "thoroughbreds" was not used. The

Thoroughbred is a particular *breed* of horse. When people speak of a thoroughbred Arabian or Quarter Horse, or when they describe a thoroughbred dog, they are using the term incorrectly. They should say "purebred." Because the Thoroughbred was the first breed of any animal to be registered systematically, the term is often used incorrectly.

For your information a list of most of the breed registries, their addresses, places of origin, distinguishing characteristics, and primary use may be found on pages 36-39. If you are interested in one or more of these breeds, you may obtain information by writing to the breed association.

THE ARABIAN HORSE

The Arabs lived in the desert with its legendary romance and intrigue. As nomad stock raisers, they depended entirely upon horses to care for their herds and flocks. The Bedouin tribes became famous as horsemen, relying upon the stamina, endurance and heartiness of their horses as a way of life. Often they brought their favorite mare into their tent at night to prevent her from being stolen.

Over a thousand years ago, the Arabs began to keep track of the "bloodlines" of their horses. The Arab (technical name of the breed) is the oldest breed of improved livestock. The first use of artificial insemination was with this horse; it has been recorded, either as fact or legend, that semen was stolen from prized stallions and raced across the desert to inseminate mares.

Desert life demanded certain special characteristics in a horse: sound feet and legs, a fleet and wiry animal which could travel over rough terrain for hours without food and water. It was not his speed but the distance he could travel in an emergency and his weight-carrying capacity which made the Arab so valuable. Since this was not a land of plenty, the Arab was smaller than our modern horses. Some Arabs today are considered small by American standards.

The Arab's most striking and distinguishing characteristics are the typical "dished" face, convex forehead with short ears, large eyes and a fine muzzle. The neck is high crested, well arched and the croup is level with a high tail set carried in a natural arch. One of the peculiarities of the Arabian horse is his short back; he has one less vertebra than other breeds.

Undoubtedly, the greatest contribution of the Arabian horse is as a source of seed stock for the foundation and improvement of the other breeds. Directly or indirectly all modern horse breeds have been influenced by this sheik of the desert.

APPALOOSA

In modern history, the Appaloosa has been associated with the Nez Percé Indians who lived in the Northwest in the present states of Oregon, Washington and Idaho. Lush summer grazing in the hills and meadows and winter forage in the sheltered canyons of the Snake, Clearwater and Palouse rivers provided excellent conditions for horse production. It is thought that the latter river is the origin of the present name. The Appaloosa obviously descended from Spanish horses. The Nez Percé improved them through selective breeding by castrating undesirable males and trading inferior stock to other tribes. However, spotted horses date back to before the time of Christ. They were known as the sacred horses of Nisaea in ancient Persia, and as the heavenly horses of Emperor Wi Tu in China.

While color is a distinguishing characteristic, there are other outstanding features of the Appaloosa. His eyes are encircled by a white sclera just like the human eye. The skin around the nostrils and lips is motley or parti-colored and the hooves have wide alternate strips of black and white. The mane and tail are usually thin, the so called "rattail." There are six basic color patterns: 1) black, white with black spots over loins and hips; 2) white, black spots over entire body; 3) bay, white spots over loins and hips; 4) black, white over loins and hips; 5) brown, white spots over entire body; 6) red roan, light over loins and hips.

The Appaloosa is noted for his stamina and endurance as well as for eye appeal because of his heritage as a war, race and Buffalo horse.

THE AMERICAN SADDLE HORSE

All horse breeds have resolved because of a special need or demand. The American Saddle Horse was developed for

Breed Association and Address	Origin of Breed
American Albino Assn. P.O. Box 79 Crabtree, Ore. 97335	United States: White Horse Ranch Naper, Nebraska
American Hackney Horse Society Room 725 527 Madison Ave. New York, N. Y. 10022	England
American Quarter Horse Assn. P.O. Box 200 Amarillo, Texas 79105	United States, in early colonies of Virginia and Carolinas
American Saddle Horse Breeders Assn. 929 So. 4th St. Louisville, Ky. 40203	United States, principally Fayette County, Kentucky
American Shetland Pony Club P.O. Box 2339 West Lafayette, Ind. 47906	Shetland Islands
Appaloosa Horse Club P.O. Box 403 Moscow, Idaho 83843	Originally Central Asia. In United States, the Nez Percé Indians in Oregon, Washington, and Idaho
Arabian Horse Club Registry of America One Executive Park 7801 E. Belleview Ave. Englewood, Colo. 80110	Arabia
Morgan Horse Club P.O. Box 2157 Bishop's Corner Ranch West Hartford, Conn. 06117	United States: New England states, especially Vermont

Distinguishing Characteristics	Primary Uses
Milk-white color, pinkish skin with blue, brown, or hazel eyes.	Parade, rodeo, and circus performance.
Traditionally shown with docked tail and pulled mane. High natural action.	Heavy harness or carriage horse.
Well-muscled in rear and forequarters. Small "foxlike" ears and large "dinner-plate" jaw.	Stock horse, pleasure horse, racing a quarter-mile.
An easy ride with great style and animation. Long graceful neck with beautiful head carriage, level croup and proud action.	Three- and five-gaited saddle horse. Fine harness horse. Pleasure horse.
Size up to 46".	Children's pony. Harness show pony. Racing pony.
Variable color pattern; white sclera encircles iris; parti-colored skin around muzzle, lip, and nostrils; vertical striped hoof.	Stock horse. Pleasure horse. Parade horse.
A beautiful head with dished face and convex forehead. Well-arched neck, short coupling, level croup. Great endurance.	Ridden both English and Western style. Stock horse. Trail riding and endurance.
Proud head carriage, neck slightly crested, short back; endurance and stamina.	Versatile. Ridden both English and Western style. Stock horse. Harness horse.

Breed Association and Address	Origin of Breed
The Palomino Horse Assn., Inc. P.O. Box 446 Chatsworth, Calif. 91311	United States: from horses of Spanish extraction
Palomino Horse Breeders of America P.O. Box 249 Mineral Wells, Texas 76067	
Pinto Horse Assn. of America P.O. Box 3984 San Diego, Calif. 92103	United States: from horses of Spanish extraction
American Paint Horse Assn. P.O. Box 12487 Fort Worth, Texas 76116	
Pony of the Americas Club P.O. Box 1447 Mason City, Iowa 50401	United States: Mason City, Iowa
(Standardbred) U.S. Trotting Assn. 750 Michigan Ave. Columbus, Ohio 43215	United States, especially Orange County, New York
Tennessee Walking Horse Breeders & Exhibitors Assn. of America P.O. Box 87 Lewisburg, Tenn. 37091	United States: in the Middle Basin of Tennessee
(Thoroughbred) The Jockey Club 300 Park Avenue New York, N. Y. 10022	England
Welsh Pony Society of America, Inc. 202 N. Church St. Chester, Pa. 19380	Wales

Distinguishing Characteristics	Primary Uses
Golden color; color of newly minted coins or 3 shades lighter or darker; with light-colored mane and tail.	Stock horse. Parade horse. Pleasure horse.
Combination of white and dark colors with many well-placed spots, white on dark color or the reverse.	Parade horse. Pleasure horse. Stock horse.
Appaloosa color with Quarter Horse or Arabian type. 46″ to 54″ high.	Large children's pony.
Smaller and less leggy, with more substance and ruggedness, than the Thoroughbred.	Harness racing, either trotting or pacing.
The running walk gait covering 5-6 miles per hour.	Plantation walking horses. Pleasure horses.
Speed and endurance. Upstanding angular, long body; deep but narrow chest.	Racing. Jumpers.
Size 43 to 56 inches. Hardy; endurance with good action.	Children's pony. Harness show ponies. Roadster and racing ponies. Hunter pony.

an easy, ambling, fast ride over long distances of rough, rugged terrain without benefit of roads. In Kentucky in the middle of the 19th century a Thoroughbred stallion, Denmark, was mated to the Stevenson Mare, a colonial-type mare by Cockspur. From this mating was produced Gain's Denmark, which had a phenomenal influence upon this breed. In developing the breed the emphasis was placed on the selection of good horses, not bloodlines; thus, the influence of the Standardbreds, the Morgans, the Arabians and the native ambling mares in addition to the Thoroughbreds is felt.

The quality of the American Saddle Horse is as characteristic as his beautiful head carriage; nicely arched, long graceful neck; short rounded back; level croup; high-set tail and his proud, stylish and animated way of going.

The three-gaited Saddle Horse, also called a "walk-trot" horse, does the three natural gaits: walk, trot and canter. The five-gaited Saddle Horse does these three plus two additional man-made gaits: the slow gait and the rack. All horsemen are thrilled at the spectacle when the announcer says, "Rack on, please." The two types can be easily distinguished by physical appearance; the three-gaited horse has a roached mane and clipped tail while the five-gaited horse is shown in a full mane and tail. In Fine Harness classes the Saddle Horse is driven to a four-wheel vehicle.

THE MORGAN HORSE

Received as payment for a debt, the small, dark bay stallion may have at first seemed more like a liability than an asset to the schoolmaster, Justin Morgan. Carrying the name of his owner, this horse was to become the sole foundation of a new breed of horses. Foaled in the last decade of the 18th century, he lived for 32 years spreading his fame throughout Vermont for his ability to outrun, outpull and outtrot all challengers.

His ancestry unknown, he clearly left his mark, especially through his grandson, Black Hawk, and his famous son, Ethan Allen. Their fame as trotters in the mid-nineteenth century greatly popularized the Morgan. However, the larger, faster Standardbreds replaced the Morgans in racing. In 1907 Colonel Battell donated his farm near Middlebury, Vermont, to the United States Department of Agriculture to preserve and improve the Morgan. The University of Vermont became the possessors of this farm and its famous herd of Morgans in 1942. A beautiful statue of Justin Morgan was erected at the farm.

Today the Morgan enjoys wide popularity as a pleasure horse. He is noted for his endurance and vigor. He has a proud head carriage with a well-crested neck, especially prominent in stallions; a deep, sloping shoulder and a short back give him a heavy-fronted appearance.

The Morgan has established an enviable record as an endurance trail horse and is shown in both English and Western classes at horse shows.

THE QUARTER HORSE

The history of the Quarter Horse parallels that of this great country. The early settlers of Virginia and the Carolinas needed a horse to work their fields, pull their wagons and double as a saddle mount. Naturally, they also wanted to race him. The Chickasaw Indians had selectively bred a short, thick versatile horse. The offspring from these Chickasaw mares, sired by imported English stallions, were superb, and exactly what the colonial Americans needed.

They became known as the American Quarter Running Horse because of their lightning speed for a quarter of a mile, usually the only straight distance available in those days. Many of these early imported stallions or their sons, such as * Janus (which was actually foaled abroad and imported later) and Sir Archy, contributed equally to the Quarter Horse and to the American Thoroughbred.

As more and more horses were imported, longer races became popular. Quarter Horses moved west with the pioneers, finally making their home and fame in the Southwest as "cow ponies." Sam Houston not only helped make Texas an independent country but his horse, Copper Bottom, was an important sire of Quarter Horses.

Identified by their unbeatable speed for a quarter-mile and impeccable ability as cow horses, Quarter Horses are heavier muscled in the chest, forearm, quarter and gaskin than other breeds. Their heads are characterized by short "fox-like" ears and large "dinner-plate" jaws. Their quiet, gentle disposition has made them the most popular horse in America today, with over 66,000 individuals registered during 1969. While famed as pleasure, roping and cutting horses, and now as hunters and jumpers, they excite millions of people annually with their blinding speed at the racetrack. The world record for a quarter-mile (440 yards) is :21.5 seconds. The world's richest horse race was run at Ruidoso Downs, Ruidoso, New Mexico, in 1970 over a distance of 400 yards with a purse of $603,000.

THE STANDARDBRED

Around the towns and cities of the eastern states the demand was for road horses or roadsters which were driven, as contrasted to their country cousins which were ridden because of the lack of suitable roads. With roadsters as with all horses, man's nature led to a desire for a faster horse than his neighbor. Drives to and from church, town, etc. usually turned into real match races to see who "ate" whose dust. Naturally, this was done in the puritan nature of the day at a trot and not a gallop, which was far too obvious.

The Standardbred evolved from this environment in the New York City area. Basically this horse was a cross of Thoroughbreds with native mares of trotting or pacing heritage.

Messenger, a Thoroughbred stallion, was a great influence. His grandson, Hambletonian, became the most famous sire of the breed. Dan Patch, who is undoubtedly one of the two most famous American racehorses (the other is Man O' War) was so fast that after being barred from competition he made exhibition appearances. It is reported that he earned in excess of $3,000,000.

Kikkulis, in about 1400 B.C., described training techniques for horses pulling chariots. But only in recent years has harness racing truly become popular. Excitement runs high while watching a field of trotters or pacers pulling a sulky and driver.

The Standardbred is different from the Thoroughbred, being smaller, larger bodied, less leggy and with more substance and ruggedness. While his primary use is racing, he is also used as a hunter and jumper.

THE TENNESSEE WALKING HORSE

Named for its native state, the Tennessee Walking Horse, as with the American Saddle Horse, was developed for an easy, comfortable, distance-covering ride. Originally used on the southern plantations, he is also known as the Plantation Walking Horse. Thoroughbred, Standardbred, Morgan and American Saddle Horse breeding make up his background. Allen F-1 is the designated foundation sire.

All individuals were selected for the characteristic gait, the "running walk." This fast, shuffling gait gives an easy, comfortable ride at a rather rapid speed of 5 to 6 miles per hour. The hind feet overreach the front feet by 14 to 22 inches. This motion results in a distinct nodding of the head.

The Tennessee Walking Horse has a thicker neck, longer back and generally lacks the quality of the American Saddle Horse, thus being more rugged.

THE THOROUGHBRED

Changing techniques of warfare in the 14th and 15th centuries required speed rather than weight carrying capacity. Thus the chivalrous knights in shiny armor were replaced by swift, flexible and evasive calvarymen. The light horses in England at that time were too small for this purpose. Attention was then focused on the Arabian, Barb and Turk because of their speed and endurance.

Many horses of these types were imported to England. Of these, three stallions are most noteworthy: Darley Arabian, Byerly Turk and Godolphin Arabian. All Thoroughbred pedigrees may be traced through the male line (son to sire to grandsire, etc.) to one of these stallions. Actually each is represented by an outstanding descendant: Darley Arabian by Eclipse, Byerly Turk by Herod and Godolphin Arabian by Matchem.

With speed as the major criterion for selection, naturally the best way to determine a horse's ability was to race him. As interest grew in this new sport, there became a definite need for a record of ancestry. In 1793 Volume I of the General Stud Book was printed; it was the forerunner of all official livestock record books.

° Bully Rock or ° Bulle Rock by Darley Arabian and out of a mare by Byerly Turk was imported in 1730 to this country from England. (An asterisk before a name denotes that the horse was foaled abroad and imported into North America.) Many Throughbreds followed ° Bully Rock to these shores especially to Virginia and the Carolinas. Thus began the development of the tremendous Thoroughbred industry in the United States.

Without a doubt the most famous Thoroughbred in recent years was Man O' War, who won twenty of his twenty-one races. In his single loss, he was second; his jockey's performance in this race still remains a controversial issue.

A Thoroughbred usually stands 15.2 hands or taller. His long, slender neck, moderate length of back and level croup along with considerable length of forearm and a great distance from point of hip to point of hock give him a long, tall appearance.

Selected primarily for racing, the Thoroughbred is also popular as a hunter and jumper. Certainly an invaluable use of the Thoroughbred in the United States has been his contribution to the development of other American horse breeds.

COLOR BREEDS

Breeds registered only on color with varying types are known as color breeds. They are popular as parade horses and for rodeo and circus performances.

THE AMERICAN ALBINO

A snow-white coat and a pink skin with dark blue, brown or black-brown eyes are the trademarks of the American Albino. The foundation sire, Old King, was believed to be of Arabian and Morgan breeding. While the early foundation mares were predominantly of Morgan breeding, today various types are evident.

The names of Cal Thompson and White Horse Ranch, Naper, Nebraska, are synonymous with that of the breed. From 1939 to 1958 a troupe traveled from the Ranch to promote and publicize the breed.

THE PALOMINO

The palomino color observed in this country today is undoubtedly the influence of horses brought to Mexico by the Spanish Conquistadores. The golden horses were extremely prized in Spain, being brought there from Arabia and Morocco.

They are usually the color of newly minted gold (with varying shades lighter or darker) with white, silver or ivory mane and tail. Their color and flashiness has led to widespread popularity; they may be observed cutting cattle or in an English Pleasure class.

Many are double-registered in their respective breed associations and also as Palominos. Well-known Palominos are Roy Rogers' Trigger and the sensational Nautical of the United States Equestrian Team.

THE PINTO

Like the Palomino, the color pattern of Pintos was introduced into North America by the Spanish. It was popular among the Indians to such an extent that they are thought of as the typical "Indian pony." They have also been referred to as paints, piebalds, skewbalds and calicos.

The horses are spotted with white and bay, brown, black, dun, sorrel or roan. There are two basic color patterns: Overo, with a primary dark color and white as a secondary color which extends upward from the belly and lower regions to form an irregular pattern; Tobiana, with white as the primary color extending downward from the back region forming an irregular pattern with a secondary dark color. Horses which are primarily white with secondary solid spots on their neck and head are known as Morocco. Glass or blue eyes are a common characteristic with Pintos.

PONY BREEDS

PONY OF AMERICAS

The Pony of Americas (POA) cannot be under 46 inches or over 54 inches thus being large enough for older children but not too small for adults to break and train. The foundation sire, Black Hand No. 1, was the result of crossing a Shetland Pony stallion to an Appaloosa mare. It was this pony which led Leslie Boomhower, a lawyer of Mason City, Iowa, to found this western pony breed in 1954.

This pony has Appaloosa color and characteristics with the type of a miniature cross between the Quarter Horse and Arabian. In performance classes he must be ridden by youths 17 years of age or younger.

THE SHETLAND PONY

The Shetland Islands which lie north of Scotland are only a few hundred miles from the Arctic Circle. Here, with spare grazing and cold climate, these ponies survived for centuries. Their original type is that of a small draft horse. In England

and Wales they are used for mining, carrying packs and light hauling. A road-type has been developed in America which has more refinement and style than the miniature draft type. Because of their heritage, they are rugged, hardy animals which require little grain or hay. A common problem with ponies on pasture is their proneness to founder.

The maximum height for registration is 46 inches (11.2 hands). They weigh from about 250 to 500 pounds. Most children have been introduced to riding on the back of a pony. In recent years harness pony racing has become an increasingly popular sport on oval tracks as a pleasant Sunday afternoon pastime.

THE WELSH PONY

From the hills and valleys of Wales this pony, whose ancestors are known only to past history, evolved. Often called the Welsh Mountain Pony, his life was not an easy one because of scarce forage, severe winters and lack of shelter.

Stallions of Arabian, Hackney and Thoroughbred breeding were allowed to roam with the herds and were mated to the native mares. Larger than the Shetland, he is classified by his height: "A" division ponies cannot exceed 50 inches (12.2 hands) while those in "B" division are larger but not more than 56 inches (14 hands). With a weight range of 450 to 600 pounds, he is ridden or driven by children who have outgrown the Shetland.

The large Welsh Pony is in demand as a hunter pony. He is also crossed with Thoroughbreds for this purpose.

COLORS

Colors and markings are important when describing a horse. Color refers not only to the body but to the *points* (which are the lower leg from the knee and hocks down), the mane, and the tail.

Bay. A body color varying in shade from light golden to reddish brown with bright red in between. Bay horses have black points or black mane, tail, and lower legs. The blood bay is a rich, dark red.

Black. Many horses are called black when they are actually brown. Check carefully the hairs in the rear flank and around the muzzle to decide which it is. A black horse has a black body without light areas and with black points.

Brown. A brown horse may be almost black, as stated above, but it has light areas at the muzzle, around the eyes, and on the rear flank. He has black points.

Buckskin. A yellowish or golden body color with black points; a form of dun.

Chestnut. A reddish body color of varying shades, with the mane and tail usually of the same shade. The mane and tail may be lighter in color (flaxen), but never black. If a light yellowish red, it is called sorrel and it may range to a rich mahogany red.

Dun. A body shade of yellow, ranging from light cream to a palomino color. The mane and tail may be black, brown, red, yellow, or mixed. There is often a darker (dorsal) stripe down the back, sometimes another (transverse) stripe crossing at the withers, and zebra stripes (horizontal dark stripes) on the backside of the leg behind the knees. A red dun horse is a reddish-orange color with a dark red dorsal stripe and a red mane and tail.

Gray. This color varies from dark steel-gray to light silver-gray, but is always composed of a mixture of white and black hairs throughout the coat. Most gray horses are born black, but a few white hairs on the backs of the ears, above the eyes, and around the muzzle indicate that a black foal will grow up to be gray. Often a gray horse is incorrectly called white.

Grullo. This is the Spanish word for mouse; it means a smooth, smoky—or mouse—color composed of individual gray hairs, not a mixture of black and white hairs. The grullo horse has black points; most have black lines down their backs and zebra stripes on their legs.

Palomino. The golden body color varies from copper to light gold, the horse has a white mane and tail that may contain a few dark hairs.

Roan. The word describes white hairs intermingled with hairs of darker color. A red roan is white and bay; a strawberry roan is white and chestnut; a blue roan is white with brown or black. Some areas may be darker than others. The roan coloring does not fade as grays do.

White. A true white horse does not change color with age or with the seasons.

Appaloosa. This spotted breed is identified by specific color patterns: spotted blanket, white blanket, leopard, frost and marble, and snowflake.

Pinto. Here the colors are in large spots or irregular patches

HEAD MARKINGS

of white with some darker color such as black, brown, chestnut, or bay, dark against white or the other way around. A *piebald* is white and black, while a *skewbald* horse is white with any other color except black.

MARKINGS

The distinctive markings of a horse are white areas on the head and legs. These may vary among individuals of the same breed. Head markings are:

Star. A white mark on the forehead.

Snip. A mark, usually vertical, between the nostrils or extending into the nostrils.

Strip. A narrow vertical mark extending the entire length of the face, from the center of the forehead to the bridge of the nose.

Blaze. A mark broader than a strip.

Bald. A broad mark that covers most of the forehead and face, and sometimes the lips and around the nostrils.

These markings are often found in combination, such as star-and-strip, for example. Principal markings on the legs include:

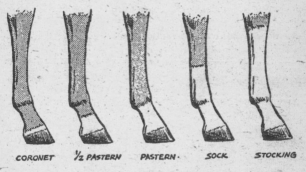

CORONET   ½ PASTERN   PASTERN   SOCK   STOCKING

LEG MARKINGS

Coronet. A narrow stripe around the coronet above the hoof.

Half-pastern. A vertical mark from the coronary band half way up the pastern.

Pastern. The same mark extending up to the fetlock joint.

Sock. An area extending from the coronary band half way up the cannon bone.

Stocking. A mark extending all the way up from the coronary band almost to the hock and knee. Both sock and stocking usually are seen on the hind legs.

AGE AND SEX

For registration purposes, all horses have the common birthday of January 1. A foal born on March 15 will become one year old the next January 1. This holds true even if a foal were born on New Year's Eve; it would be "one year old" on the next day. Consequently, when a race is announced for three-year-olds, none of the horses entered may be older than three years, counted in actual months of life—but some may be only two and a half years old or even younger.

A *colt* is a male horse up to three years old.

A *filly* is a female horse up to three years old.

A *foal* is a *colt* (male) or *filly* (female) under one year old.

A *mare* is a mature female horse.

A *stallion* is a mature male horse.

A *gelding* is a male horse castrated before reaching sexual maturity.

A *stag* is a male horse castrated after reaching sexual maturity.

A *stud* is a farm where stallions are kept for breeding purposes.

HEIGHT AND WEIGHT

The height of a horse is measured from the highest point on the withers to the ground. The unit for measuring height is the *hand;* a hand equals four inches (about the average width of a man's hand). A 15-hand horse stands 60 inches high. Any additional inches are put after a decimal point: 15.2 hands equals 15 hands plus 2 inches, a total of 62 inches. Do not be confused by this if you need to do any arithmetic; that is, 15.2 does *not* mean 15 and two-tenths.

The weight of a horse can be estimated by a veterinarian or by any experienced horseman. For an exact figure, ride the horse to a local feed dealer who has a scale. A study at Louisiana State University indicated that the average mature Quarter Horse, standing 15 hands, weighs approximately 1,200 pounds.

Chapter 5

Selecting Your Horse

Each breed of horse has its group of enthusiasts. In this author's opinion, however, a good horse is a good horse regardless of breed. You should learn to appreciate a fine pony or a well-built draft horse for that matter. The most important consideration in selecting a horse is to decide what you plan to do with it.

You might be enchanted with a racehorse, but in most cases a horse bred only for speed would be too high-strung to be a satisfactory pleasure horse. You would not buy an outstanding show winner in the three-gaited class and expect to make a top roping horse of him. Nor would you buy a Western type of broodmare with the idea of begetting a line of harness track champions.

The kind of performance expected of a horse helps you to eliminate the unsuitable. Concentrate your attention on finding the desired characteristics in an individual horse.

There are four basic aids that are used in the selection of horses: pedigree, conformation, performance, and progeny. The genetic principles of selection are discussed also in the chapter on improving the breed. (See pages 171-75.)

Pedigree ranks as an important consideration when the horse is young, or when you are seeking traits which have a rather low heritability. As you will see, the fact that a colt is a great-great-great-great-grandson of Man O' War can mean very little. The facts of genetics are much more complicated than that. The mare's side of the pedigree rates equally with the stallion's in determining the legacy of the foal.

51

Proof of performance rates higher as a consideration as the horse matures. If you want a horse to score well in jumping, pleasure riding, roping, or reining, certainly you will choose one with the best record and one you can afford. Naturally, the price of a green hunter or of a green-broke Western pleasure horse will be lower than for a blue ribbon winner. If you do not have the money to buy a proven horse, the emphasis in selection shifts to the pedigree and to the conformation of the animal itself.

If you are buying a mare or a stallion for breeding purposes, a major factor is the record of previous offspring. A proven sire or a proven dam is one whose progeny have demonstrated their winning ability in the show ring or on the racetrack. If you decide to raise a foal for pleasure riding, then you should buy a mare whose foals regularly turn out to have a quiet disposition and good riding qualities. The mare herself need never have been ridden at all.

The conformation of the horse is paramount where performance and/or progeny records are unavailable. Here you are on your own. How does the animal look? You can see with your own eyes, but you must know what you are looking for. There is a direct relationship between form and function. This chapter will give you some pointers on judging a horse.

THE IDEAL HORSE

Much has been written and many opinions have been voiced on the ideal conformation, that is, the body shape and structure of a horse. This ideal applies to all breeds of horses, despite their differences. A good shoulder on a Thoroughbred would also be a good shoulder on a Quarter Horse. Broadly speaking, Western horses are more muscular than English horses; otherwise breed differences are noted mostly in the head and neck.

What does a judge of horseflesh look for, aside from the type characteristics specific to a particular breed? Study the illustration showing the parts of a horse so that the terms will be familiar to you. A judge uses a scorecard in examining the major areas, based on 100 points for the perfect animal. The following is this author's assignment of points by categories:

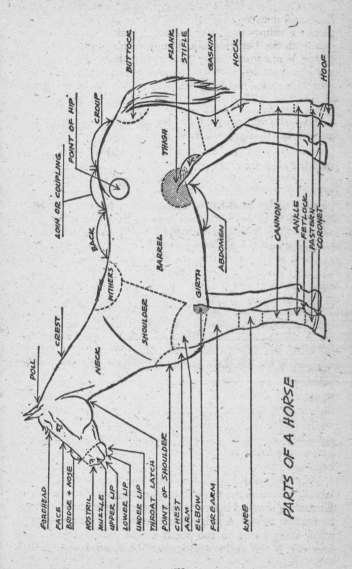

PARTS OF A HORSE

POLL
CREST
NECK
WITHERS
SHOULDER
BACK
LOIN OR COUPLING
POINT OF HIP
CROUP
BUTTOCK
FLANK
STIFLE
GASKIN
HOCK
HOOF
THIGH
BARREL
ABDOMEN
GIRTH
CANNON
ANKLE
FETLOCK
PASTERN
CORONET

FOREHEAD
FACE
BRIDGE + NOSE
NOSTRIL
MUZZLE
UPPER LIP
LOWER LIP
UNDER LIP
THROAT LATCH
POINT OF SHOULDER
CHEST
ARM
ELBOW
FOREARM
KNEE

Category	Points
General Appearance	15
Head and Neck	7
Forequarter	22
Body	13
Rearquarter	33
Way of Going	10
	100

Notice the emphasis on the forequarter and rearquarter; this includes the feet and legs.

GENERAL APPEARANCE

Balance

Look first for good balance. The various parts of the horse should be in proportion to one another and all parts should look as if they belong to the same animal. His head and neck should not be too long for the rest of him, or vice versa. This is important for performance as well as for looks. A properly balanced horse will be well coordinated—he will be easier to train and will give a smoother, more comfortable ride than one whose poorly matched parts lead to awkward, clumsy movements.

The center of balance is just behind the forelegs in the area of the heartgirth. Notice how jockeys ride forward so that they are directly over this point. The horse can run faster when the weight is evenly distributed over the center of balance.

Quality

Signs of quality—an indication of good breeding—include a fine, glossy hair coat; skin pulled tightly over the muscles and bones, best observed on the lower legs; and especially good bone.

In cross section, a good bone on a horse is oval rather than round. Look at the cannon bone; it should appear wider from the side than from the front. Flat, clean, hard bone is stronger and will stand up better under hard use.

Smoothness

Closely related to balance is smoothness. The neck blends smoothly into the shoulder, for example, and the coupling into the rearquarter.

Style and Type

The stylish horse moves and stands gracefully and is alert. He looks his type, too, according to breed. You should not select an American Saddle Horse type when looking for a Western pleasure horse, or the reverse.

Size

As a rule, if you see two animals of identical conformation, you should select the larger of the two. Within the limitations of the breed, the bigger animal generally has the advantage in performance.

HEAD AND NECK

Although the head of a horse is his most prominent feature, and many owners look at little else, we give this area only 7 points out of 100. Besides clear, bold eyes and good width between them, with medium length from the eye to the muzzle, the main thing to check is the horse's ability to breathe. The horse as a performance animal requires lots of oxygen to get the job done.

The nostrils should be large since he cannot breathe through his mouth. Try to place three fingers between the jawbone and the neck muscle. If you cannot, the horse's air supply may be restricted when he is turned or stopped. Jawbones set too close together may constrict the windpipe of the horse.

The jaw should be well developed for strength, medium size in a mare, but more massive in a stallion. The neck should be of medium length, slightly arched, and blend smoothly into the shoulder. A short, thick, cresty neck greatly reduces a horse's maneuverability.

FOREQUARTER

The horse's shoulder is an important indication of the comfort and ease a rider can expect from a horse. It is part of the horse's shock absorber system and relates to the shortness, thus to the strength of the back and to the length of the underline, and thus to the length of the strides. The angle and length of shoulder are both to be considered.

Drop an imaginary vertical line to the point of the shoulder and then horizontally toward the rear, bisecting this angle from the point of the shoulder to the top of the withers producing a 45-degree angle for an ideal shoulder. A long shoulder with proper angle means a shorter back and a longer underline, therefore a longer stride; the horse with a long shoulder can bring the front legs well forward for a good stride.

The chest should be deep and fairly wide, indicating a good constitution and lung capacity, important for a performance animal. The width of the chest is the distance from point of shoulder to point of shoulder. The muscling in this area varies with the breed. However, it should tie down into the knee on the inside of the foreleg as well as outside; these muscles move the foreleg forward and pull it back. The arm should be short, muscular, and carried well forward.

The forelegs carry 65 percent of the horse's weight. The illustrations show the correct position of the front leg from the front and side. Conformation of the knees, which should be wide, deep, and straight, is most crucial, since deviation from normal in any direction may indicate weakness in support.

Foals are often buck-kneed; that means the knee is bucked forward or over in the knee. It puts strain on the ligaments and bone. The condition should disappear by six months of age. The opposite condition, calf knees, with the knee too far back, causes even more trouble. Horses may also be knock-kneed (knees too close together) or bowlegged (with knees too far apart). The off-set or bench knee does not line up with the center of the cannon bone, and the horse will be prone to develop splints.

The terms base-wide and base-narrow refer to the distance between the front feet at the ground. Both conditions may lead to unsoundnesses. (This will be described in the next chapter.) Other deviations that may be observed alone or in association with the above-mentioned conditions, and which occur in the fetlock, pastern, and hoof, are "toeing-in" or "toeing-out." Either condition is very undesirable, as it relates to predisposing unsoundnesses such as sidebone and ringbone. The horse that toes-out (splayfooted) breaks over on and lands on the inside of the foot and therefore wings when traveling. A horse that toes-in (pigeon-toed) breaks over on

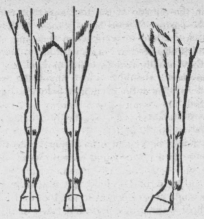

FIGURE 1—Front and side views
of ideal forelegs.

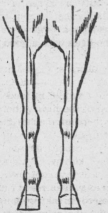

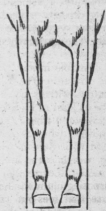

FIGURE 2—Toe-out conformation.

FIGURE 3—Toe-in (base-narrow) conformation.

and lands on the outside of the foot and thus paddles when traveling. The narrow-chested horse is most likely to be base-wide which causes him to wing when traveling. A base-narrow condition is observed in horses with large, heavy muscled chests and they usually paddle when moving.

The cannon bones should be short, broad, flat, with sharply defined tendons. The fetlocks should be wide, straight, and well supported. The pasterns, which are part of the shock absorber system, should have a 45-degree angle, be smooth, strong, and of medium length.

The foot should be of a size in proportion to the body. It makes no sense for a 1,200-pound horse to wear a size o shoe. The front should be round, with a slope of about 45 degrees to the foot and pastern. The hind foot is slightly longer than wide, with a slope of 50 degrees to the foot and pastern. Obviously the hoof walls, frogs, and other parts of the foot must be strong to bear the weight of the animal.

BODY

The body of the horse is extremely important as it is the area which contains the lungs, the stomach, the intestines, and many vital organs. Since the horse is a performance animal, he requires a tremendous quantity of oxygen. Therefore great lung capacity is necessary. The same thing is true for the digestive system since he consumes a large quantity of feed daily. The heartgirth should be deep with a good spring of rib.

Most desirable in any horse is a short, straight back—the strongest structure. The withers should be prominent, since flat "mutton" withers will not hold a saddle in place. They should be at least as high as the top of the hips. A horse that slopes downward from croup to withers approaches the sway back condition, which is as weak as it looks.

The last rib should be close to the rearquarter so that the coupling, which is the area over the kidney, is short. Some riders believe, incorrectly, that a heavy weight or blow at this point can injure the horse's kidney. The real problem is not the kidney, but structural strength at the coupling since it is muscle, not bone, which unites the rearquarter to the body.

REARQUARTER

While the forelegs support most of the weight, the hind limbs produce the power that propels the horse. The rearquarter is his "engine compartment." To provide a short back and a long stride, as discussed with the shoulder, the croup should be long and moderately level. The length of the croup is from the point of the hip to the point of the buttocks. Too steep a croup means a short underline.

Western type horses are more heavily muscled than English horses, especially in the quarter, stifle area, and gaskin. In all horses the quarter should be deep and the inside and outside muscles of the gaskin should tie down into the hock. Long driving muscles, measured from point of the hip to the hock, combined with a short distance from the hock to the ground, produce the most power. The hocks should be free from fleshiness and have the shape of an upside down teardrop. Deviations in shape or position lead to unsoundnesses. The illustrations show the correct positions of the hindleg viewed from the rear and side.

FIGURE 4—Ideal hindlegs. A line dropped from the point of the buttock bisects the limb.

FIGURE 5—Ideal hindlegs from side view.

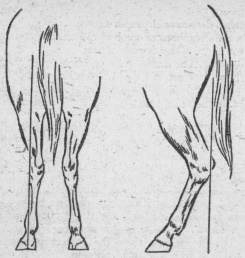

FIGURE 6—Cow hocks accompanied by base-wide conformation.

FIGURE 7—Sickle hocks. Note the excessive angle of the hock joints.

Most horses toe-out a little with their hind feet; if this brings the hocks too close together (cow hocked), it is objectionable, otherwise it is normal. A sickle hock is one that makes too much of an angle with the line from the buttock. A boxy hock is as wide at the bottom, or nearly so, as at the top of the hock.

WAYS OF GOING

The horse reveals a lot by his way of going. Draw an imaginary line out ahead of him from the center of each front foot. As he moves forward, he should place front and rear feet on the corresponding straight line. The walk should be rapid, flat-footed. Listen to the rhythm; the cadence should be regular if the horse plants his feet solidly, without hesitation.

If the horse is slightly lame, he may not show it at the walk, but he will at the trot. The beat of the gait should be perfectly even; otherwise the horse may be favoring one foot. The trot should be straight, smooth, springy, free, and with no extreme kneefold. From the side, look for a flight of the foot in an even arc. Each foot should break squarely over the toe and the heel should land just before the toe, putting the center of weight at the point of the frog.

Variations in the ways of going are usually due to conformational defects or improper shoeing.

Here are definitions of some of the terms describing defective ways of going that horsemen use:

Cross firing. The inside of the hindfoot scuffs the inside of the diagonal forefoot; this is usually seen in pacers.

Forging. The toe of the hindfoot strikes the sole of the forefoot on the same side and up to the pastern in extreme instances.

Interfering. A foot in motion strikes the fetlock of the supporting leg on the opposite side. Horses that toe-out, or that are toe-wide or base-narrow, are apt to do this.

Paddling. The horse throws his feet outward as he travels. The foot breaks over and lands on the outside of the toe. Horses that toe-in or are base-narrow tend to paddle.

Pointing. The horse stands with one leg in front of the other, bearing as little weight on it as possible. This is done in an effort to ease the pressure on a sore leg and it can be observed most frequently in racing Thoroughbreds and Standardbreds.

Scalping. The toe of the front foot hits and scrapes the hairline on the hindfoot of the same side. It may also hit the pastern or cannon bone.

Speed cutting. A form of interference among the feet which occurs at high speeds. It is most generally observed as an injury to the hindleg between the coronet and fetlock.

Winding or rope walking. The striding leg twists around in front of the supporting leg. This is often observed in wide-chested horses.

Winging. An exaggerated paddling noticed in high-stepping horses.

GAITS

The horse has three natural gaits: the walk, the trot, and the gallop. Other gaits are either man-made or natural modifications of these three gaits and usually have been selected for a special purpose within a breed. The five-gaited American Saddle Horse is trained to do the unnatural rack and a slow gait, usually the stepping pace. The Tennessee Walking Horse, instead of trotting, is characterized by its natural running walk. Many Standardbreds pace rather than trot.

In explaining these gaits, with the help of the illustrations, the following abbreviations for the four feet will be used:

R—right	L—left
F—fore	H—hind

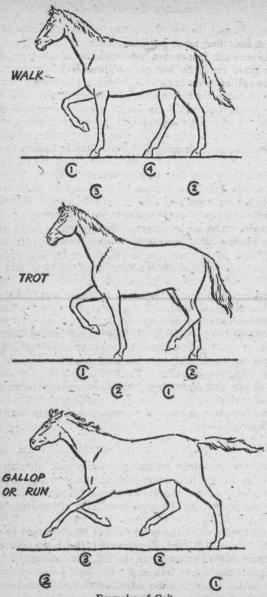

Examples of Gait

The *walk* is a four-beat gait. A well-trained horse should walk at least four miles per hour, about the same speed as a fast hiker. Each foot moves independently of the other three. At all times the horse has two or three feet in contact with the ground; he never has all his weight on one foot.

The walk should be straight, true, easy, with a good stride. At the walk you can immediately check the horse's stride. This is the distance between two successive prints made by the same foot. A long stride enables the horse to cover a greater distance with less effort; it is equally important at all gaits.

The *trot* is a two-beat gait in which the diagonal pairs of legs hit the ground simultaneously. The RF and LH feet move forward together, and the LF and RH feet move forward. In a trot, all four feet may be off the ground during a brief moment in each sequence.

The *pace*, a little faster than the trot, is similar to the trot except that the feet on the same side move together. The sequence might be RF and RH, then LF and LH.

In the *gallop*, a three-beat gait, the horse attains his greatest speed—up to 40 miles per hour for a distance of a mile or less. The sequence might be the LH foot strikes the ground, then the RH and LF feet together, then the RF foot makes the third beat. In a very fast gallop, as seen at the racetrack, the RH and LF feet do not hit simultaneously. The hind foot strikes ahead of the diagonal forefoot, and thus sounds as a four-beat gait to the ear.

The *canter* is a restrained gallop. Western riders use a medium-fast gallop called the *lope*. It is rhythmic and comfortable for range riding, since both horse and man can keep it up for long distances without tiring. A *run*, as observed in race horses, is a fast gallop.

In all forms of the gallop, the two unpaired legs, which function independently, bear more weight and are therefore subject to more fatigue than the diagonally paired legs. To remedy this situation the lead is changed frequently. A lead is the corresponding movement at a gallop of the legs on one side.

A left lead is when the left fore- and hindlegs lead or work together. In a left lead, for example, the horse can circle more smoothly and sharply to the left. The correct lead, left lead when circling to left, and right lead when circling to right, allows a horse to be coordinated and to make sharp turns with ease and agility. The wrong lead results in a ride that is less smooth.

These have been general points of comparison that apply to practically all horses. To learn more about the breed that interests you, write for the literature of the breed association and study its illustrations carefully. You will find that each places emphasis on particular conformation—such as the head, neck, and croup—that distinguishes one breed from another.

Unsoundnesses that are to be avoided in selecting a horse will be discussed in the following chapter.

Chapter 6

Is Your Horse Sound?

Soundness is the single most crucial factor in appraising a horse. We often hear the saying, "No foot, no horse." Technically an unsoundness is any deviation from normal structure or function of the horse. Our concern here is with serious conditions that affect the serviceability of the animal. On the other hand, some abnormalities, usually man-made, are blemishes that do not interfere with the usefulness of the horse. They may diminish his value, but a slightly blemished animal with otherwise good qualities may be a genuine bargain.

Some horses inherit faulty conformation and this is a predisposing factor to certain unsoundnesses. For example, those with hereditary sickle hocks are more likely than others to develop curbs and spavins. Overwork also can lead to unsoundness, especially in racehorses trained at too early an age. Poor nutrition, particularly in minerals and vitamins, may result in poor bone growth and thus, in weak feet or legs. By reason of their active, nervous nature, horses are prone to accidental injuries that may result in an unsoundness.

An unsound horse is like an athlete with tender feet: out of the running. An injured man can continue to hobble around and make a living in some other way, but a horse may have to be destroyed. That is why unsound conditions of the feet and legs are a matter of utmost concern. The following brief descriptions tell how to recognize and avoid them, and also, if they can be treated successfully.

Founder. Correctly called laminitis, it is the most painful horse disease short of acute colic. The animal can barely put his feet to the ground. When it is acute, the feet (most often the forefeet) are hot to the touch because of the blood congestion within them. The shoes must be removed and the horse persuaded to stand in a tub or a stream of cold water. The hoof wall grows more rapidly than normal, and the toe may curl up at the end. Heavy rings formed on the wall are telltale signs of founder.

Inflammation of the sensitive portions of the wall and the sole of the foot seems to be the result of a variety of disorders; one might say the foot is the horse's weak spot. Grain founder comes from eating too much grain, grass founder from too much lush pasture, in particular, clover and alfalfa. This is especially true with overweight horses and ponies. Treatment of the digestive upset aims to remove the cause of founder in these cases.

Still another type strikes a mare after foaling as a result of retention of a portion of the fetal membrane (afterbirth) or an infection of the uterus. But one type, road founder from concussion, you certainly can avoid. Never run a horse on a hard surface!

Even if the foundered horse recovers, he may never be suitable for anything but light work. A new technique, using plastic to replace parts of the damaged hoof, shows promise as a cure.

Splints. Common to most young horses, there are bony enlargements of the splint bone, usually on a foreleg on the inside, just below the knee. While the splint is forming, the area becomes swollen, hot, and painful, and the horse goes lame. In time the injury hardens and the horse may return to work without serious hindrance. Sometimes a splint disappears altogether; various treatments are effective. A horse with bench (off-set) knees is subject to splint, because his odd stance puts a greater strain on the splint bone. Concussion and strain are typical contributing causes, especially as a result of working young horses on sharp turns. A lack of or an improper balance of calcium, phosphorus, vitamins D or A, may result in splints.

Sidebone. (For detailed description of the hoof see "Care of the Feet," Chapter 8.) A horse's hoof has elastic cartilages, like springs, on each side of the coffin bone. Their function is to assist in the expansion and contraction of the posterior part of the hoof and to pump venous blood up the leg. When one of the cartilages becomes bony, the horse has sidebone and may go lame. Concussion is the usual cause (again beware of hard surfaces), abetted by dry feet, lack of frog pressure and poor shoeing. Horses that toe-in are prone to develop lateral (outside) sidebones while those that toe-out tend to develop medial (inside) sidebones. However, in both cases, sidebone may develop in both cartilages. The horse must be rested until the initial inflammation subsides. Corrective shoes will help by rolling the foot away from the affected side. Growing a larger hoof which is wider in the heel helps cure sidebone. Rasp off side walls of the quarter of the hoof, thinning it to help to reestablish frog pressure.

Ringbone. Inflammation of the bone covering (periosteum) results in ringbone which is growth of new bone in a ring around the pastern. The forefeet are most commonly affected. Ringbone effectively cripples the horse; treatment is difficult and not always successful, rest being one of the best methods. A horse that toes-in or toes-out, or one that has a straight pastern, puts greater than normal stress on the joint, and thus is susceptible to ringbone. Overexertion of a young, immature horse may have the same effect. Shoeing off the level results in tipping the foot too quickly or to an exaggerated degree; it is also a major cause of ringbone.

Bowed Tendon. Caused by a severe sprain, the tendons behind the cannon bone become inflamed and swell. Bowed tendon is described as a telescoping of the tendon sheath, the attachments of which are torn from their position causing hemorrhage and inflammation. This is more common in the foreleg. The horse stands with heel elevated to ease the pressure. If treated before a fibrous scar forms, the horse may recover after a long rest. Very little can be done later. Horses with long, weak pasterns, calf knees, or too much weight are prone to bowed tendon. Forced training, high speed, and exertion or improper shoeing, can also cause it.

Osselet. The animal *points* a forelimb (holds the foot advanced forward of the leg) because of an inflamed fetlock joint resulting from a rupture of the joint capsule from its attachment in the joint. This sort of inflammation rarely appears in the hind legs. Lameness is usually apparent; the area is hot and painful. The ankle becomes enlarged because of the continuous concussion of hard training, especially in two-year-olds. Osselets seldom occur in horses that are accustomed to hard work gradually. Horses with straight pasterns are more apt to develop this condition. Firing or blistering sometimes helps, followed by paints and absolute rest for about four weeks.

Spavins. A bog spavin is a soft (not bony) swelling of the natural depression on the front and inside of the hock caused by an excess accumulation of the lubricating joint fluid. The horse usually does not go lame, unless the spavin is large with heat and pain. It may be due to a sprain, often curable by daily massage with a liniment for two to three weeks, bandages, diet, and rest. But if the horse is of faulty conformation —too straight in the hock, or with thick, coarse hocks—the bog spavin will often recur.

A bone spavin is a bony enlargement on the inside and front of the hock; it is more medial, about one-half inch lower than the bog, and more serious. A jack spavin is an unusually large and well defined bone spavin. The immediate cause may be an injury, especially from quick stops as in roping. Horses with narrow, thin hocks, sickle hocks, or cow hocks are predisposed to it. Lameness, which is worse when the animal is first used, may disappear with exercise. Removing a portion of the cunean tendon where it crosses the spavin area removes the source of pain. Corrective shoeing may be beneficial. The horse will go sound even with a large bone spavin after the affected bones have fused together.

Curb. A horse that kicks the tailgate of his trailer or the wall of his stall may develop a curb. The curb, an enlargement or bulge, forms below the point of the hock on the back of the hind leg. It is caused by inflammation and by a thickening of the plantar ligament which holds the cannon bone and the bones of the hock in position. Horses with sickle hocks or cow hocks are predisposed to this condition. Rest is absolutely necessary. Lameness and inflammation usually occur at the initial development but sometimes disappear.

Toe, Quarter, or Heel Cracks (Sand Cracks). These cracks in the wall of the hoof are growing either upward or downward and are results of inadequate trimming, injury, or dryness and weakness in the hoof. The name tells the location in the various sections of the hoof wall. The horse may go lame if the crack extends into sensitive tissue. To correct this condition, a pattern is grooved into the end of the crack to limit its progress, like this: $\underline{V}$ or a groove is rasped across the top of the crack: T. Also, corrective shoeing should be used, and the crack cleaned daily with tincture of iodine if an infection is present.

Thoroughpin. A thoroughpin is a swelling which occurs at the back and on top of the hock in the area known as the hollows, immediately in front of the point of the hock. It does not respond well to treatment but is seldom serious enough to cause lameness. It is due to a chronic inflammation and excess accumulation of fluids. Rest is important.

Corns. Horses, like people, can get corns on their feet from improper or worn-out shoes. They occur most frequently on the inside of the front feet at the angle formed by the wall and the bar and appear as reddish or bluish areas. The horse will favor the sore spot by putting more weight on the opposite side of the foot or on the toe. Removal of the shoe may be all that is necessary. If shoes are left on too long the heels of the shoe bruise this area. Improper shoeing by trimming out too much of the supporting bars has the same effect. If the corn becomes infected, it should be drained and treated by soaking in an antiseptic or solution of magnesium sulfate daily. Bandage the foot to protect it from contamination.

Blemishes. Small wounds and bruises must be expected of horses used for hunting, jumping, and roping, or even engaged in the usual "horseplay" in a pasture. These wounds often leave blemishes. Wire cuts, rope burns, blister scars, and saddle sores may disfigure a horse somewhat, but they will cause him no more trouble than the scars on the face of a prizefighter. The following blemishes, however, are caused by inflammation and may be mistaken for more serious unsoundness.

Windpuffs or Windgalls. These are small, firm, fluid swellings that occur just above, and occasionally behind, the fetlock. Usually there is no lameness. Young horses in heavy training get windpuffs, and once developed, they remain for life. Liniments and rest for a few days may help reduce the initial swelling.

Capped Hocks. Quite common today, this swelling of the point of the hock comes from a blow, generally by kicking a stable wall or trailer tailgate. Although the horse may not be lamed, the cap is an unsightly blemish. Treatment aims at reducing the swelling before a fibrous cap forms.

Capped Elbow or Shoe Boil. Very similar to a capped hock, but less common, this inflammation comes from the horse bruising the point of an elbow with a front shoe or from lying down on a hard floor. The point of the elbow becomes swollen. The treatment is the same as for capped hocks, in addition to having the horse wear a shoe-boil boot to prevent recurrence.

Some guidelines to avoid unsoundness:

1. Select only horses with good conformation of feet and legs.

2. Do not overexert young horses.

3. Do not ride a horse faster than a walk on hard surfaces.

4. Condition your horse by proper exercise before hard riding.

5. Feed him a balanced ration at all times.

6. Eliminate potential causes of accident or injury.

7. Shoe horses, if necessary, regularly and properly.

8. Clean and inspect the feet of stabled horses daily.

9. At the first sign of lameness or unsoundness, call your veterinarian.

Chapter 7

Owner's Guide to Good Management

Some people think a horse "delicate," not realizing that almost everything that can happen to impair his health is imposed upon him by his master. Horses are rugged, hardy animals, well able to take care of themselves. They have proved it by surviving as a species for more than 50 million years. In domesticating the horse, human beings have taken on the responsibility of his survival. And this responsibility is called management. The true horseman differs from "just a horse owner" by the way he manages his horse. A pleasure horse, as kept under present conditions, probably needs more care than almost any other animal.

Feeding, a part of good management, is so important both to health and economics as to warrant three chapters. (See pages 87-125.) Chapters 7 and 8 deal with the other things every owner should know and do in order to keep his horse healthy, happy, and a pleasure to ride.

SHELTER AND EQUIPMENT

Far from being "delicate," a horse living outdoors can get along fine with only the natural protection of trees or hillsides. His body produces heat to keep him warm in cold weather; and it also produces heat when he becomes extremely hot. He must be kept dry and out of drafts, however. A horse faces away from the wind and rain and lowers his head, thus exposing only his hindquarters and top line.

Any building used to shelter a horse must also protect him against dampness and wind. In many climates a three-sided, open shed will do nicely. The tradition of stabling dates back to the horse-and-buggy days when owners wanted their horses handy, just as we want our cars handy today. A small stable may consist of a single row of stalls with a covered shed

71

row, or work area, or two rows of stalls with an alleyway between them.

A main consideration in a stable is good ventilation. A "tight" barn will keep horses warm, but the air becomes stuffy and the horses often get sick. Experts estimate that each horse needs from 1,200 to 1,600 cubic feet of space with the air changed from eight to ten times each hour. Windows that hinge at the bottom and open inward from the top provide good ventilation without drafts.

A draft is a current of air, not necessarily cold in itself, but it feels cold when it strikes the skin. Chills and shivering are caused when the blood near the surface areas is driven to the internal organs. Drafts are especially dangerous when the horse is damp. Windows and doors, besides being draft-free, should be screened on the outside against insects and protected on the inside with heavy wire.

A box stall gives a horse more freedom to change position or lie down to rest than does the old-time tie stall. Preferred sizes are 10' x 10' and 10' x 12', or for mares with foals and for stallions, 12' x 12' or 14' x 14'. A tie stall may be 5 or 6 feet wide, and up to 9 feet long including hay manger and feed box. Ceiling height for any stall should be at least 8 feet.

Whether of wood or concrete blocks, the walls and partitions should be smooth and free from projections such as splinters and nails. Five-foot high solid partitions are recommended, with two feet of slats, bars or heavy wire above them. This provides for ventilation and allows horses to see each other; they enjoy company. Rough concrete walls can be covered with plywood.

Kinds of flooring are important in stable construction. Clay makes the best floor since it is firm, safe, and quiet; it helps keep a horse's feet soft. Clay requires maintenance, as some horses paw, making the floor uneven. For sanitary purposes, 2 to 4 inches of clay should be replaced each year. Plank floors are warm and springy enough, but they are noisy and also unsanitary since they tend to absorb urine. A pawing horse will also wear out a plank floor. Concrete, while sanitary, easily cleaned, and long lasting, becomes slippery and is too hard—it has no give. It causes horses to "stock up," accumulate tissue fluid resulting in swelling. Concrete alone is unsatisfactory as a floor; however, a good compromise is a concrete floor covered by a wooden frame which may be removed for cleaning.

All light bulbs in the stall should be recessed in a metal

covering in the ceiling with a heavy wire protector. Heat lamps, which are used in foaling stalls in colder climates, should also have protective covering.

Removable feed tubs made of metal, plastic, or rubber are better than built-in feed boxes because they are easier to keep clean and disinfect. Hay nets are popular because they can be moved and set at any height. With a hayrack a horse may get dirt in his eyes; if a net is set too low he can get his feet caught. A hay manger should slant outward from bottom to top to protect the horse's knees. Set the manger height at 38 to 42 inches. Never feed hay on the floor; it's both unsanitary and wasteful.

If you use water buckets, they will need refilling two or three times a day. Automatic watering saves this work. Horses should never be without water. There is no danger of over-watering except when the horse is heated up from exercise, and there is no loss of feed or nutrients no matter when he drinks. Wash and disinfect water buckets regularly.

Plan adequate storage space in the feed room, loft, or in an extra stall. You can save money by buying hay, grain, and bedding in quantity at the time of harvest when they are lowest in cost. This chart will help you measure the space required:

Material	Storage Space Per Ton (cubic feet)
Barley	51
Corn, shelled	44
Oats	77
Hay, baled	80–200
Shavings, baled	100
Straw, baled	167
Straw, loose	512

BEDDING

Bedding is extremely important in stalls for protection, comfort, warmth, and sanitary purposes. Several materials may be used as stall bedding; each has advantages and disadvantages. Provide an adequate amount of bedding, remove it regularly and add fresh bedding as necessary.

Long the standard horse bedding, straw absorbs about two and one-half times its own weight in urine. Straw is the mature stem and leaf portion of cereal-grain plants such as oats, rye, barley, and wheat. It should be clean, dry, bright, and free from mold. About 10 pounds of fresh straw daily will be needed to replace soiled bedding.

Sawdust is a fairly good substitute, especially with a horse that insists on eating the straw. If too fine, however, it may be dusty. Soiled sawdust ferments, and must be removed quickly before it gets hot and attracts flies.

Wood shavings are less absorbent than sawdust, and should not be used if they contain blocks or chips of wood that might injure the horse. Sand, a good bedding in hot, dry climates, gets too cold where there is dampness. Also a horse may get a serious colic from consuming the sand. Don't ever use ocean beach sand which the horse might lick for the sake of the salt.

Other bedding materials include dry peat moss, corncobs, peanut hulls, oat hulls, and pine needles. Whatever you use, keep it sanitary by removing all manure daily and replace the soiled bedding with a fresh, clean supply.

MANURE

Disposal of manure is a key aspect of management if you want to prevent diseases and control the parasites and insects that plague your horse. "Muck out" the stall every day when removing the manure and soiled bedding.

Never spread fresh manure for fertilizer on a horse pasture; this merely spreads the parasite eggs contained in it. It may be safely used on crop land, or on pasture grazed by cattle or sheep. Horse parasites do not infect these other species.

Better yet, store the manure in a pit or open pile for at least two weeks. Fermentation produces heat which will then destroy the infective eggs. In the open pile, turn the outer layer each week about six inches deep to insure proper fermentation. A double-sided and floored manure box with cover will help to overcome the problems of odor and insects.

Chapter 8

Care Any Owner Can Give

GROOMING

At times grooming may seem to you to be routine drudgery, but it is essential for a horse's good health as well as his appearance. Grooming not only cleans, it removes waste products, prevents skin diseases and parasites, stimulates the circulation of blood and lymph, improves muscle tone, and helps gentle the horse.

Those areas where the horse sweats most freely require the most attention. The function of the sweating is to cool the body and remove waste products. Sweat appears first at the base of the ears, then on the neck, next along the sides of the chest, back, and hindquarters—never on the lower part of the legs. Salt from the sweat dries and may be observed as white material in the flank areas and over the croup.

Another secretion, the sebum, prevents penetration of harmful substances, protects against external moisture, and gives the horse its characteristic gloss. In cold weather the hairs stand on end, trapping body heat like a blanket around the body. Here are some of the various grooming tools:

Curry Comb. Either rubber or metal, it is used to remove long, thick hair, especially in the spring. It removes caked mud and dirt, also. Use it gently in a small circle. Never curry on bony parts, such as the head or lower legs below the knees and hocks. Never use it on horses with very fine hair or on a horse recently clipped; it can irritate the skin.

Body Brush. Made of stout bristles or vegetable fibers with a loop for the hand, it removes dandruff and dirt. The *dandy brush* has stiff, two-inch bristles for caked dirt; never use it on the head. A *water brush* has longer, finer, and softer bristles and may be used on the bony parts; you wash the feet and legs with it or dampen the mane and tail.

GROOMING SUPPLIES

CURRY COMB

BODY BRUSH

DANDY BRUSH

MANE AND TAIL COMB

SWEAT SCRAPER

HOOF PICK

GROOMING CLOTH

TOWEL

Mane and Tail Comb. Usually of metal, it is used to comb out tangled manes and tails.

Grooming Cloth. From 18 to 24 inches square, it can be made of an old towel or a woolen blanket. Use it to wipe out the eyes, ears, nostrils, lips, and sheath, or to remove fine dust and dirt from the coat. A sponge may serve the same purpose, but it may become a means of spreading infection. With a

76

well-groomed horse, the water brush and this cloth will be all you need for a final polish.

Sweat Scraper. A long, flexible blade of smooth metal, it is used like the windshield wiper of a car to wipe off excess sweat or water. One can be made from a discarded fine-tooth hacksaw blade by taping each end for handles and bending it in the shape of a U for use.

Hoof Pick. An essential tool, since the feet need cleaning daily. An old dandy brush (or other stiff brush) is handy for finishing the job begun by the hoof pick. Hoof dressing keeps the hoof moist and growing, and adds a shine for the show ring.

Electric or hand clippers and/or scissors are useful in removing excess hairs from the ears, fetlocks, mane, bridle path, and lower jaws.

HOW TO GROOM YOUR HORSE

A stabled horse should be groomed at least once a day. Groom him lightly just before exercise, and thoroughly afterward. It takes at least thirty minutes for a general or light going over. It will take up to one hour for an extremely dirty or sweaty horse, or one shedding his winter coat in the spring. You can make the job easier for yourself by following this set procedure:

The horse must be cool and dry. First remove dried mud, heavy dirt, and sweat with the scraper, curry comb, or dandy brush. Next, using the curry comb and brush, or just a brush, start on the left side of the neck back of the ear (the horse is used to having you at his left), brush with the lay of the hair, toward the rear and downwards. However, you can use a circular, backward or crosswise motion where dirt, mud, or sweat is stubborn.

Proceed in this order: the neck, chest, shoulder, wither, foreleg down to the knee, back, side, belly, croup, and hindquarter down to the hock. Cover the right side in the same order.

As you go, clean the brush constantly with the curry comb. Curry gently, brush vigorously. Stand back, hold the brush with a stiff arm, apply weight to the brush giving it a flick of your wrist to remove the dirt.

Use a soft brush on the head, finishing up around the eyes, ears, nostrils, and lips with the grooming cloth. Comb out, then brush, the mane and tail. Wipe the body with the grooming cloth; if necessary, use a wet sponge or water brush to remove the fine dirt.

Now clean each hoof with the hoof pick, and brush them to remove loose particles. (See foot care, below.)

Wash and disinfect the grooming equipment at regular intervals, especially if the horse has been sick. Take care of any small wounds (see Chapter 13), and the job is done for the day.

DOES HE NEED A BATH?

Race horses commonly get a washing when lathered up after a race, but a bath is not a shortcut to good grooming. Never wash a horse unless he can be thoroughly dried, as he is susceptible to chills. If, especially in hot weather, you feel a bath is called for, since horses sweat and lather up when ridden, here is what to do:

Get three buckets of warm water. In one of them, add a wash mixture or mild laundry detergent. A special wash mixture containing lanolin is good since it restores some of the natural oil washed out of the skin. Work up a lather all over the horse's body, rubbing against the hair with a brush or with your hands. Rinse with a big sponge, using the water in the remaining two buckets unless a commercial non-rinse product has been used. Proceed from the head to the neck, back, sides, rump, chest, front legs, belly, inguinal area, hind legs, rearquarter, and tail. After rinsing, remove excess water with the scraper but do not use on legs or head, and sponge up the remaining water with a clean sponge.

Finally rub the horse as dry as possible with a rag, and cover him with a sheet or blanket, depending upon the weather. Cool out the horse as described on page 80.

TRIMMING

Trimming usually depends upon the breed and use of the horse, as some breeds are shown with a short mane and tail. It does not hurt a horse to pull out the mane and tail hairs. It is better to pull out a few at a time than to cut them; it produces a more even, uniform appearance. Take some hairs together with the thumb and index finger of the left hand, then grasp the ends of a few hairs with the same fingers of the right hand. Push the left hand up with the rest of the hairs, and give a quick jerk with the right hand pulling out three or four hairs. Do not do too many at one time since the mane or tail may become sore.

Sometimes the mane refuses to lie down on one side of the neck. You can paste the hair down with water or a little wet clay. If this does not work, take a two-foot length of broomstick, cut it in half lengthwise, place one half on each side of the mane and fasten together. This weight will make the mane grow on the desired side of the neck.

Clip the ears for show purposes by folding the ear and cutting off all long hairs. Don't disturb the hairs inside the ear, since they keep out dirt and insects. You can remove the long hairs on the jaw and fetlock with scissors or clippers.

Western horses usually have their manes roached, leaving the foretop and a tuft of hair at the wither. The tail is usually pulled so it extends to the top of the hocks. Hunters usually have their manes braided, with a thinned tail and braided dock, or upper part of the tail. Three-gaited American Saddle Horses are shown with clipped mane and the first five inches of the tail shaved from the base, while five-gaited Saddle Horses have a full mane and tail, with only the foretop and first lock of the mane braided.

These have a practical origin. For example, a full mane on a Western horse may result in entanglement of rope, mane, and rider's fingers—more than one cowboy has fewer fingers because of such mishaps.

EXERCISE

Quite possibly you own a pleasure horse for the sake of the fun and excitement of riding in the open air and showing. But it is also good for your health, especially for anyone troubled by overweight. Horseback riding at the trot requires more calories per minute of activity than swimming 20 yards per minute, walking at the rate of 3.75 m.p.h., golfing, cycling at the rate of 5.5 m.p.h., bowling, and many other popular forms of exercise. The same applies to the horse. He needs exercise for good health, and a well-formulated plan of exercise that is mutually beneficial to both is an important phase of good management.

Condition of a horse refers to physical fitness for the performance required; this implies a good state of health, vigor, and muscular tone. Condition is indicated by brightness of eye, alertness, bloom to the coat, absence of fat, and a characteristic hardness of the muscles. It is a matter of degree. Extreme examples are the race horse and the overfat show horse.

Excess feeding and insufficient exercise add up to a fat horse. He will be out of condition for the performance you desire. When ridden far or hard, he sweats profusely, breathes heavily, and may get seriously ill. You can't expect him to stand in a stall all week and gallop with fire and dash on Sundays only.

You can observe fat accumulating first on the neck, withers, over the ribs, back, and croup. Realize also that fat is gathering around vital internal organs of the body. To keep a horse in good condition, you must balance the amount of feed he receives with his exercise.

Most exercising should be done at a walk and trot—at least forty-five minutes of walking, with fifteen minutes of trotting, for a minimum of one hour per day. If the horse is badly out of condition, walk him only, for about a week. It will take about six weeks to get a horse in good condition.

Once conditioned, one or two hours of exercise per day are necessary to maintain him in a physically fit state. Exercise obtained in a pasture will suffice for a broodmare or young horse, but a riding horse needs more exercise. Several miles a day of alternate walking and trotting will do it, or else the shortcuts to conditioning called ponying and longeing.

In ponying you ride a "pony" horse while leading the horse being exercised. Racing mounts often are kept in condition this way. The longe line is a long rope attached to the halter; the horse makes a circle around the person holding the line. The circle may be 30 or 40 feet in diameter. The horse should travel one way and then the other at different gaits. This method often is used with animals too young to be ridden.

Work, as contrasted to exercise, refers to riding that will cause some effort on the part of the horse; it would include a Sunday ride, riding in a show, or schooling.

After riding, let the horse walk on the way to the stable so that he will be dry when you arrive. If the horse is wet after exercise, he must be cooled out to prevent a chill. Remove excess moisture with a metal scraper. Rub him down briskly with your grooming cloth until he is partially dry, and blanket him if the weather requires it. Then walk him for twenty to forty minutes until he is thoroughly dry. The chest is the last place to cool so check it with your hand. Allow him only a few swallows of water at first, then more as he becomes cool. A properly cooled-out horse is not hot to the touch nor is he breathing hard.

If this seems like trouble, remember that conditioning one's horse also conditions the owner! You will benefit as much as the animal from a planned exercise schedule in your good management program.

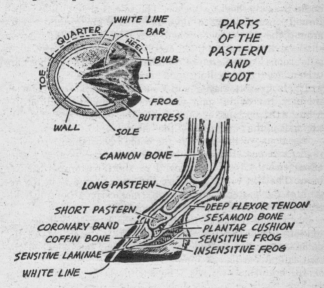

PARTS OF THE PASTERN AND FOOT

CARE OF THE FEET

The foot is composed of four parts: the hoof, the bones, the elastic structure or cartilages, and the sensitive structure or corium. The hoof is a horny, tough substance and consists of four parts: the wall, bars, sole, and frog. The hoof provides a protective covering for the inner sensitive parts; it has no nerves or blood supply. The wall, which is the only part you see when the foot is on the ground, grows like a fingernail. The outer layer of the hoof wall is composed of the *periople*. It covers and extends about ¾ of an inch below the coronary band where it becomes the *stratum tectorium* whose primary function is to retard evaporation of moisture from the foot. It also gives the glossy, shiny appearance to the wall of the hoof. Because of this protective nature of the outermost layer, the wall should never be rasped higher than the nail clinches. The hoof wall is divided into three sections: the toe which is the area between the first nails on each side; the quarter which is from the first to the last nail, and the heel which is from the last nail back.

Picking up the foot, you can see the bars extending at an angle from the heel to the toe. The sole is shaped like a dish turned upside down; it does not touch the ground except around the edges, where there is a white line. This concave shape gives a good foothold and bears the weight better than a flat sole (like the arch of a human foot). Nails for shoes are driven into the white line, which is not sensitive.

The frog—soft, elastic, and V-shaped—can be seen between the bars. It provides some resistance to slipping and dissipates a lot of the concussion since it hits the ground first. This action aids in the circulation of the blood.

The bones of the hoof are the coffin bone (third pastern or phalanx bone), the navicular bone or distal sesamoid, and about two-thirds of the second or short pastern (phalanx) bone. The first or long pastern (phalanx) bone is in the region of the pastern. The cannon (metacarpal) bone extends from the knee and hock to the fetlock joint.

The elastic tissues of the foot are the lateral cartilages, extending upward and backward winglike on each side of the coffin bone, and the plantar cushion that lies between the two lateral cartilages, under the coffin bone and over the sensitive and horny frogs. The lateral cartilages and plantar cushion are part of the shock absorber system of a horse's foot. Their primary function is to reduce concussion to the foot; posteriorly they form the bulbs of the heels.

The sensitive structure or corium nourishes the foot and is made up of the following: the periople; the coronary band; and the sensitive laminar, sensitive sole, and sensitive frog, which are the mirror image of the horny wall, sole, and frog, respectively. Each of the horny structures grows from the sensitive portion which is rich in blood vessels and nerves.

The heel makes contact with the ground slightly before the toe does; the heel expands because of the action of the frog and this helps to distribute the concussion. The frog is forced upward into the plantar cushion which expands sideways since the second pastern bone prevents expansion upwards. The pressure of the plantar cushion is exerted against the lateral cartilages which cause an expansion of the quarters of the hoof. The foot may expand ½₅ inch, which indicates its flexibility. These changes are essential for the health of the foot. The contraction and expansion of the foot acts as a pump to aid in the return of the venous blood to the heart. This provides better circulation which increases the flow of nutrients to the foot and removal of waste products. When the foot hits the ground, the wall, bars, and the frog bear the weight. Only about one-quarter of the sole on the inside of the white line should bear weight.

The hoof wall grows downward about three-eighths inch per month, and must be trimmed every four to six weeks. In nature the growth usually equals the wear. But in unshod horses, foreign material collects in the crevice of the frog and in the cracks between the side of the frog and the bars.

As previously mentioned, a stabled horse should have its feet cleaned daily, before and after each ride, as part of regular grooming. If the foot becomes too dry, sometimes the result of lack of exercise or of dry weather, it may crack or the frog loses its elasticity. Hoof dressing helps combat this.

Use a hoof pick to clean the hoof, working it from the heel toward the toe, to avoid the risk of penetrating the frog. Clean the area between frog and bars, also the crevice of the frog. Check the shoes, if any, to make sure they are not loose.

Shoeing is a necessary evil of domestication, to prevent the foot from wearing faster than it grows. The shoes usually need replacement, or at least resetting, every four to six weeks. This is a job for blacksmiths; persons without the necessary training or experience should not try to shoe a horse. Horses should not be turned out to pasture for long periods of time with shoes on.

Many of the leg problems seen in horses (and there are a lot of them) can be traced to neglect of the feet, especially when the horse is very young. When does one start a foot-care program for a foal? When it is one month old. Proper trimming at this early stage can avoid later unsoundnesses which are the results of toeing-in, toeing-out, or similar defects. You can prevent a lot of problems by keeping the foot clean, moist, and properly trimmed and/or shod—and by starting this foot care program early.

TEETH AND THEIR CARE

Whether yours is a "gift horse" or not, you should definitely look at his teeth! They're important to him for grasping and chewing feed, and to you as a check on his age. In the wild state the teeth were also a means of protection. This does not imply that domestic horses don't bite. Most people who have been around horses for a long time would rather be kicked than bitten by them.

Stallions and geldings have 40 teeth: 12 front or incisors, 4 canine or tusks, and 24 cheek or premolars and molars. Mares usually have 36 teeth, normally they do not have the tusks. These are located in the space between the front and cheek teeth. Occasionally they will erupt (break through the skin) in a mare and cause a sore mouth. A foal has temporary milk incisors (front teeth) in three sets: the center or nippers, at birth or within ten days; the intermediate, on each side of the nippers, within four to six weeks; and the corner teeth, within six to nine months. The horse has a full mouth at five years when all the front teeth are permanent.

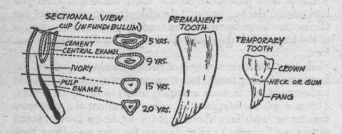

The parts of the tooth are shown in the illustration. As the horse ages, the temporary milk teeth are replaced by permanent teeth that will wear with age. The star of the tooth appears; then the cup disappears. Teeth change shape gradually, becoming triangular; in advanced age rectangular. Here is a table of the changes in the front teeth that will aid you in determining your horse's age:

Eruption and Wear of Teeth in Years

	Nippers	Intermediate	Corner
Temporary teeth wear	1	1½	2
Permanent teeth	2½–3	3½–4	4½–5
Table surface wears	6	7	8
Star appears	8	9	10
Cup disappears	11	12	13
Shape changes	14	15–16	16–17

TEETH OF THE
THREE YEAR OLD COLT

TEETH OF THE
SEVEN YEAR OLD HORSE

Another aid in determining a horse's age is Galvayne's groove on the upper corner tooth. It appears at the gum line at ten years, advances half-way down the tooth at fifteen, and reaches the wearing surface at twenty. Then it retreats half-way down the tooth at twenty-five and it completely disappears at thirty. For mules, add three years to all the figures in the table, because the enamel of their teeth is harder.

"Bishoping" was an old-time swindle practiced by horse traders to make the animal appear younger. They would grind false dental cups into the lower front incisors. More authentic dentistry is concerned with the following:

Floating. The process of removing sharp projections on the cheek teeth that interfere with chewing or may damage the tongue and cheeks, especially of older horses. The cheek teeth tend to wear sharp edges on the inside of the lower teeth and the outside of the upper teeth, resulting in a horse that eats extremely slowly, lets feed fall out of its mouth, or holds its head to one side while eating. Floating is a simple job utilizing a special rasp.

Toothache. It is rare in horses, but it can occur through decay or inflammation of the roots. While eating or drinking water, the horse will suddenly stop chewing, throw its head to one side, and open its mouth slightly. Extraction is the remedy.

Wolf teeth. The first permanent molars are usually removed because they may be a source of irritation and a hindrance to training.

Parrot Mouth. The upper jaw is longer than the lower jaw, giving the horse a parrot-like beak when viewed from the side. The teeth do not meet properly and the horse has trouble eating. It is something to avoid in selecting a horse, especially for breeding, as it's hereditary.

To prevent undue pain to your horse and many more serious problems, have his teeth checked at least once a year.

CARE OF TACK

Tack refers to the equipment used on a horse: saddle, bridle, halter, harness, etc. It is generally expensive even if purchased as used tack. Care of tack, therefore, is essential for prolonged usefulness, safety, and comfort to the rider and horse. Proper care can also help decrease the spread of disease.

Leather is used predominantly in making most tack, so care of tack actually involves care of leather. Even though leather is perishable, it can be used for many years with proper treatment. There are saddles being used today made prior to 1900!

Leather should be kept dry and clean and should be cleaned each time it is used. Dirt and sweat should be removed by washing with saddle soap or castile soap. Use a medium-wet sponge to avoid making the leather too wet or soggy. The leather should be dried thoroughly with a chamois. To keep the leather pliable, neatsfoot oil, or leather dressing should be applied. Store tack in a dry area. (The dampness of a stable can be detrimental to leather.) Never place leather near a fire as it tends to dry it out. Dry leather becomes stiff and brittle and will crack.

While cleaning the bridle, the bits should be washed and disinfected. Metal polish should be used on all metal parts.

One should be careful in selecting tack, and choose for quality. Stirrup straps should be sound and strong enough to hold your weight. Check for weakness and wear, especially in used tack, around buckles, rings, and attachments. The threads of stitching will wear out before the leather, especially if they become dry. Particular attention should be given the stirrups leather, girth, and bridle reins.

Chapter 9

The Whys of Horse Feeding

In the wild state, horses and similar animals seldom stay long in one place. They graze continually but will take off nervously at the slightest disturbance or when beset by enemies. Evolution has adapted the species to this "eat and run" existence.

Like a cow, a horse can subsist on grass and hay. But unlike the cow, which is a ruminant, he does not chew his cud. He has no compound stomach for the breakdown of fibrous plant material into nutrients. He has only a simple stomach like man and the dog. Why, then, can a horse digest hay, although we can't? The answer is because of his special type of large intestine.

This is but one of many fascinating aspects of a horse's unique digestive system. With an understanding of equine nutrition, the owner can do a more efficient job of feeding, which is the key to good management.

Equine nutritive needs are similar to our own: carbohydrates, fats, proteins, vitamins, minerals, and water. The way the owner proportions these nutrients in the feed will affect the horse's performance and appearance.

HOW A HORSE EATS

In grazing a horse uses his strong upper lip to place blades of grass into position between the front teeth. These incisors cut off the grass as efficiently as a lawn mower and closer to the ground than a cow's teeth. In the manger, loose grain is grasped by the lips with the aid of the tongue. The next step, chewing, is extremely important for proper nutrition and cannot be rushed.

The teeth crush grain kernels and divide grass or hay into fine particles. Saliva mixes with the feed for easier chewing and swallowing. The salivary glands in the mouth of a horse produce an amazing amount of saliva—about 10 gallons every 24 hours. That's one reason why he needs a lot of water. An active horse will drink 8 to 12 gallons a day.

The proper amount depends, in part, on the type of feed. Oats will absorb their own weight of water: 6 pounds of oats plus saliva will equal 12 pounds. But hay will absorb four times its weight: 6 pounds of hay plus saliva will equal 30 pounds.

A horse chews from side to side as well as up and down. Because of this, the upper jaw is wider than the lower jaw; thus, horses chew only on one side at a time.

A slow eater by nature, a horse needs fifteen to twenty minutes to eat a pound of hay, and five to ten minutes for a pound of grain. Normally most of the hay portion of his ration is fed him at night to allow enough time for chewing. If a horse eats too fast—and some do—he can suffer from colic just like a child. Should your horse gobble his food, try one of these remedies:

1. Feed him smaller amounts of grain and more often.

2. Spread out the feed in a thin layer on the bottom of the manger, so he can pick up only a small amount at a time.

3. Place large smooth stones, about the size of a softball, in the manger to force him to select his mouthfuls more cautiously.

THE THROAT: A ONE-WAY STREET

The alimentary canal of a horse is a tube of prodigious length, extending from mouth to anus. There are dissimilarities to the digestive system of man; for example, man can breathe through his mouth, while a horse cannot. Also, man may cough up objectionable materials without serious consequences. We often swallow something that "goes down the wrong way," but a similar mishap would result in serious consequences for a horse. It is very difficult for him to vomit.

Here are the consequences if he tries to vomit:

1. The feed will be forced out through the nostrils in a snort or sneeze, since it cannot be ejected through the mouth.

2. The pressure may cause a rupture of the stomach.

3. The material, if forced back into the pharynx region, may go into the windpipe and thence into the lungs, causing pneumonia. The last two could be fatal.

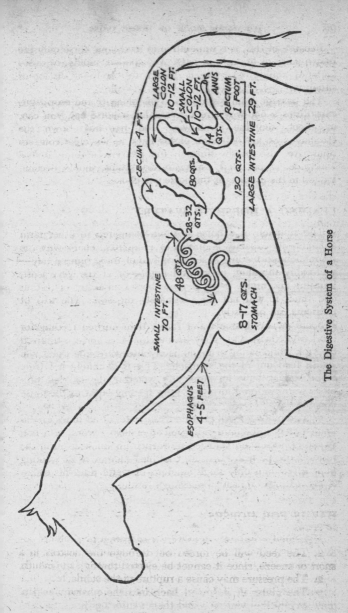

The Digestive System of a Horse

Labels within figure:

LARGE COLON 10-12 FT.

SMALL COLON 10-12 FT.

CECUM 4 FT.

RECTUM 1 FOOT

ANUS

14 QTS.

80 QTS.

28-32 QTS.

130 QTS.

LARGE INTESTINE 29 FT.

48 QTS.

SMALL INTESTINE 70 FT.

8-17 QTS. STOMACH

ESOPHAGUS 4-5 FEET

Because of this, it is imperative to feed your horse only the best quality of grains and hays. Any spoiled, moldy, or dusty material could make the horse try to vomit—a disastrous situation.

The passage from his mouth to his pharynx and esophagus constitutes a one-way street. Watching a horse eat, you can, in effect, see the swallowed feed traveling down the esophagus on the left side of his neck in wavelike contractions. Air also passes through the pharynx enroute to the windpipe. If any feed, especially dry grains, should become lodged in the esophagus the horse will choke.

LEADING A HORSE TO WATER

The stomach of a horse is small compared to other farm animals—its capacity is only 8 to 17 quarts. That's why the recommended feeding schedule is two or three times a day—preferably morning, noon, and night—or at the very least, morning and night. If we give our horses an excess of feed at one time, it will not be adequately digested. The loss of nutrients can be costly.

Some owners blame water rather than hurried feeding for the loss of thriftiness. They believe that if a horse is allowed to drink while eating or immediately afterward, the water will "wash feed out of the stomach." This is definitely not true. Some stables have an automatic watering device that provides water before, during, or after feeding—just as the horse chooses.

A good manager will provide fresh water at all times *except* immediately after hard riding or other heavy work. If a hot, sweating horse were allowed to quench his thirst at once, the result could be colic. Instead, cool him out slowly by walking him. Allow him only small amounts of water until his excessive sweating and heavy breathing subside.

HAY IS FOR HORSES

The small intestine continues the digestion of proteins begun by the stomach. It also breaks down starches, sugars, and to some extent, fats. Digestive juices are supplied by intestinal glands: the pancreas and the liver. The part of the feed that is digested may be absorbed through the intestine into the bloodstream and carried to all parts of the body.

The alert reader will note a significant omission: a horse has no gall bladder. In most other mammals this organ stores up bile for release into the intestine as needed to emulsify fats. In the horse, bile is secreted continually in the small intestine. There is no reserve supply of bile at the proper time to aid efficiently in the digestion of fat.

The large intestine provides the key to the horse's ability to subsist upon grass and hay. It consists of the following regions: cecum, large colon, small colon, rectum, and it terminates at the anus. It takes a lot of roughage to match the nutritive value of a small amount of concentrated feeds, such as grain.

Actually the horse cannot digest cellulose (the fibrous part of roughage) under his own power. No mammal can. It is broken down with the aid of friendly bacteria that live in the cecum and large colon. Dwelling in the large intestine, these microscopic plants transform cellulose into energy-yielding volatile fatty acids. They also manufacture the B vitamins necessary to life, and amino acids out of which usable proteins are formed.

Digestion is completed in the colon and the remaining water is absorbed in the small colon. The undigested residues here are formed into the characteristic balls of feces. A horse normally voids 33 to 50 pounds of feces a day.

NUTRIENTS IN HORSE FEEDS

A good balance of nutrients is as important in feeding horses as it is in the human diet. Each has specific functions for the support of life. All are essential and none is more important than the others.

Except for water, the largest portion of a horse's ration consists of energy-supplying nutrients: carbohydrates and fats. Energy feeds act as fuel for the body, just as gasoline fuels an automobile. They are necessary for muscle movement, such as the beating of the heart, breathing, walking, or running, and to keep the body warm in cold weather. They power the numerous chemical reactions of the body.

ENERGY

The carbohydrates, by far the major source of energy in the horse's ration, include sugars, starches, and cellulose. Oats, barley, and corn may contain 60 percent sugar and starch; thus they are considered concentrated feeds. Cellulose, the fibrous material found in the hulls of oats and barley and in all roughage, is less efficiently digested and utilized, and must be eaten in far greater amounts.

Fats as a source of energy for horses are not very important since the horse cannot efficiently digest them. Normally, horse rations contain little fat. Fats aid in the absorption of fat-soluble vitamins. Any excess amounts of carbohydrates and fats will become body fat, to be stored for future use as energy. The saying that the eye of the master fattens the animal is certainly true of horses. Body fat will first be observed deposited on the neck and withers, then over the back and ribs, and finally over the croup. Normally there is little fat in the muscle tissues of the horse, and none of the marbling that appears in beef.

Excess fat is undesirable. It should be removed before the animal is given strenuous exercise or training. Excess fat is (1) detrimental to the horse's health; (2) it interferes with his performance; and (3) besides, it is costly. You should be able to detect when your horse begins to get too fat, or when he starts to lose weight. Either is your cue to make an adjustment, down or up, in the amount of energy-producing feeds in the daily ration.

PROTEINS FOR MUSCLE

Protein, which is made up of small components called amino acids, is used primarily to build and repair tissue. Most of the protein in feed goes into the horse's muscle. It also helps form bone, blood, skin, hair, and hooves. The last two are of particular interest. Lack of protein in the feed could result in poor hoof development and a poor hair coat.

When should protein supplements be fed? In spring when the horse sheds his winter coat, a little extra protein can help hasten the growth of new hair. When a young horse is growing, when a mare is in late pregnancy or nursing a foal, the protein content of grains and hay usually is not adequate. Vegetable oil meals (soybean, linseed, or cottonseed) may then be added to the ration.

Excess proteins, like excess carbohydrates, find their way into body fat. This is an expensive proposition since protein feeds are costly.

VITAMINS

Thanks to wide publicity, most horsemen are probably better aware of vitamins and minerals than of other nutrients. Actually these are neither more nor less vital than the other nutrients. Although vitamins and minerals are mixed in commercial vitamin-mineral supplements, the two are not the same.

Vitamins are organic (nonmineral) compounds which are required in small amounts to regulate chemical reactions within the body. Vitamins are in two categories: (1) fat soluble—vitamins A, D, E, and K; (2) water soluble—the various B vitamins and vitamin C (ascorbic acid).

All good quality green forages are rich in most vitamins required by the horse. Pasture is extremely valuable from this point of view. Where it is limited, only the finest quality hay should be fed. Vitamin supplementation has become a common practice, especially with breeding and growing animals and with those in training or performance.

Vitamin A. This vitamin does not occur as such in plants. Animals derive it by eating carotene, the yellow coloring compound found in various edible plants, such as carrots. The yellow in cream and butter comes from carotene. Holstein milk is whiter than Jersey or Guernsey milk, showing that the Holstein converts more carotene to vitamin A.

Vitamin A is essential for the health of the digestive, respiratory, and reproductive tracts. An animal suffering from vitamin A deficiency would be prone to digestive upsets such as colic; to respiratory ills such as coughs, colds, and runny nose; and to reproductive failure and abortions. Vitamin A is important to the eyes for the prevention of night blindness, and poor hoof growth has been known to develop for lack of it.

Green, growing pasture is the best source of carotene. A normal ration with a good amount of green leafy legume hay gives a horse an adequate amount of carotene. The carotene of grass hay is not as well utilized and should be supplemented. Vitamin A is a relatively inexpensive supplement to add to the diet. Species and breed differences are known to exist in the conversion of carotene to vitamin A.

Research conducted at Rutgers University College of Agriculture, New Brunswick, New Jersey, indicates that blood carotene or vitamin A levels are directly related to the pasture season. There is a rise in blood levels with the spring grazing season, a drop in the dry summer pasture season, and an increase again with fall pasture. The long winter non-pasture season results in a definite continual decrease. While the grazing season will vary in other areas, the pattern will follow the pasture season. Fat-soluble vitamins can be stored in the body but obviously the vitamin A stores will be depleted during the winter months. Based upon these data a vitamin A supplement should be fed during the winter, dry summer months, periods of drought, or when pregnant mares do not have a source of pasture. Horses may not be as efficient converters of carotene to vitamin A as was previously thought.

Vitamin D. Commonly called the sunshine vitamin, it is actually produced in the skin by the action of the sun's rays. This vitamin would not normally be lacking in horses kept out on pasture during sunshiny days. It plays an important role in the conversion of calcium and phosphorus to body use, especially in the formation of bones.

A vitamin D supplement in the ration may be necessary in winter periods without sun, or where horses are stabled. A deficiency produces rickets in young horses and a similar condition in mature horses, called osteomalacia. Good sun-cured hay usually supplies vitamin D, but hay cured to the point that it is completely brown is undesirable from a quality standpoint.

Vitamin E. This vitamin is a controversial subject in the horse world. Research has shown that rats cannot reproduce if fed a diet deficient in vitamin E. Would this have the same effect on horses? The best evidence indicates not. On the other hand, vitamin E definitely is required for the development, function, and maintenance of muscle. The normal horse ration supplies it; but in periods of stress such as rapid growth, late gestation, training, or racing, a commercial supplement such as alpha-tocopherol may be beneficial.

Vitamin K. This is an essential component of the blood-clotting mechanism and is normally adequately synthesized in the intestinal tract of the horse. Without it the animal would be vulnerable to even the slightest bleeding, as in human hemophilia.

The B vitamins. As described earlier, they are synthesized by bacteria in the horse's cecum and large colon. What's puzzling, however, is that absorption occurs in the small intestine—upstream from the area where produced. The degree of absorption leads to the unresolved question as to the horse's ability to utilize the B vitamins which are synthesized in his large intestine. The B vitamins are: thiamine (B_1), riboflavin (B_2), niacin, pyridoxine (B_6), pantothenic acid, biotin, choline, folic acid and B_{12}. The B vitamins function in association with enzymes in energy and protein metabolism. While only limited research has been done with B vitamin nutrition in horses, the data indicate that B vitamin deficiencies may occur and supplementation is necessary. Thiamine (B_1), riboflavin (B_2), pantothenic acid and B_{12} supplementation has each been beneficial under certain conditions. For instance, riboflavin deficiency has been associated with moon blindness. B_{12} deficiency causes anemia in horses.

Vitamin C. This vitamin (ascorbic acid) is synthesized by the horse. Some reports indicate a correlation between poor breeding quality and a low level of vitamin C in the blood.

Vitamins are required in small amounts and the fat-soluble ones may be stored in body tissue. Feeding excess amounts of fat-soluble A, D, E, and K could be dangerous and result in calcification of soft tissue with vitamin D. If you use a vitamin supplement, feed it at the manufacturer's recommended level. Do not feed two or three different supplements; this is not a case of a little bit being good and a lot more being better.

MINERALS

Minerals are inorganic elements, that is, not produced by living things. Like vitamins, they are required in small amounts. In nature the horse gathers minerals by eating plants that store them. The major minerals of primary concern are calcium, phosphorus, magnesium, sodium, chlorine and potassium. Others are found as mere traces in very minute quantities and include iodine, cobalt, copper, iron, zinc, and manganese.

The average ration contains an adequate supply of trace elements, except that iodine is known to be lacking in certain areas, the "goiter states." This lack in a pregnant mare's ration may result in foals born dead or very weak. The solution is simple: feed iodized salt.

Other trace minerals, such as iron, are deficient in particular states; check with your local agriculture agent or state college of agriculture. If there is any doubt or question, feed trace mineralized salt.

Calcium and Phosphorus together are the major components of bone. As a performance animal, the horse depends upon good feet and legs—a combination of bone and muscle. Lack of these minerals may be a factor in unsoundness. Ninety-nine percent of the calcium in the body is in bone and teeth; 80 percent of phosphorus is also in the skeleton. Magnesium is closely associated with calcium and phosphorus with 70 percent of its content being in the skeleton.

Proper bone nutrition is particularly important today because young horses are subjected to great stress. Yearlings are trained for the racetrack. Even with pleasure horses, most owners cannot wait until the horse nears maturity before breaking and training. But the mineral requirements of a young horse are different from those of a mature horse—a fact not generally taken into consideration.

In the mature animal, bone analysis shows two parts of calcium to one part phosphorus. Therefore, the ration should also be 2:1. But in the young, growing animal, the ratio in the bones is 1:1, equal parts of calcium and phosphorus. The young horse needs approximately twice as much phosphorus, in proportion to calcium, as the mature horse because phosphorus is essential in the soft tissues.

Roughages are relatively high in calcium and the grains supply phosphorus. Vitamin D is important here because without it the calcium would not be absorbed, throwing off the calcium-phosphate balance. Both may be supplied in steamed bone meal or dicalcium phosphate.

Sodium Chloride. This is, of course, common salt. Because of his work, a horse needs more salt than other farm animals, about three ounces a day. A pound of sweat contains about two grams of salt. Give your horse free access to a block of salt or supply it in a granular form. Otherwise, salt may be mixed directly into the daily ration in the proportion of ½ to 1 percent by weight. Sodium, chloride and potassium are important in the fluids and soft tissues of the body. They regulate water metabolism and the passage of nutrients into the cells.

Excessive amounts of minerals could be dangerous and more likely to be a problem than excess vitamins. An example would be excessive levels of calcium which could lead to calcification of soft tissue. There also may exist a relationship between overfeeding and unsoundnesses. Do not oversupplement, follow the manufacturers' recommended level.

WATER AS A NUTRIENT

An animal can live much longer without feed than without water. Water is the cheapest nutrient available and there is no excuse for failing to supply it in abundance. A constant supply of fresh, clean water is one of the best signs of a good horseman.

The body of a mature horse contains about 50 percent water, while that of a newborn foal contains about 80 percent. A horse drinks more or less according to the heat of the season, the amount of work he does, and the kind of feed.

Water is primarily a carrier, the "workhorse" of metabolism. The blood, largely water, carries nutrients from the digestive system to all parts of the body, picks up waste products, and helps eliminate them.

Water serves as a built-in cooling system in warm weather by carrying off excess heat. In cold weather it conserves heat to keep the body warm. It also acts as a lubricant, especially in the joints.

WHICH NUTRIENTS AND WHEN?

There is a vast difference between merely maintaining a horse, as in nature, and working him at duties. Even in nature, reproduction of the species, growth, and suckling of the young impose special demands for nutrients. An animal may be in several categories at one time. A mare giving milk to a foal often is pregnant and may be doing a considerable amount of work as a riding horse. A young, growing horse, two or three years old, may also be in training. These are physiological requirements of the body.

Maintenance is defined as supporting the absolutely necessary body functions, basal life, plus normal activity. Some of the basal needs are blood circulation, heartbeat, breathing, digestion and maintenance of muscle tone. Normal activity includes grazing, chewing, lying down, getting up, walking, romping, and playing. Man-made pleasure riding, jumping, roping, etc., constitute work.

A good example of a maintenance state is the idle, pleasure horse during the winter. One hour of riding per day is considered within the limits of maintenance.

Horses in certain areas of the West and Southwest, kept on pasture the year around, receive only a maintenance ration. In the spring and summer when grass is abundant, they get more nutrients than needed and deposit them as body fat. In the winter when there is less grass, this fat is burned up as energy.

Horses need higher maintenance rations than cattle because they are more nervous. The "easy keeper" that stays in good condition with less feed usually is quiet and docile. Nervousness that consumes energy is especially prevalent in racing breeds.

Plenty of good quality hay, alone, provides a maintenance ration. If the hay is of lower quality about two pounds of grain may be added. On legume or good mixed hay the horse may gain weight, indicating that the ration is above maintenance level. Good pasture of well-fertilized, mixed legumes and grasses will usually keep horses in excellent condition. Sometimes they will even get too fat.

A rule of thumb: A horse in maintenance condition will usually eat about 2.5 percent of body weight in good hay. Thus a 1,200-pound horse will consume 30 pounds of hay per day.

NEEDS OF THE GROWING COLT

Growth describes the state of the suckling, weanling, yearling, and two-year-old—actually on up to three and four years old. A horse reaches maturity at about five years, a fact that was respected in the Western range country. There, horses ordinarily were not broken or trained until three or four. Today under pressure of economic demands, breaking and training often start at less than two years, especially with racing animals. The combination of rapid growth and work imposes exceptional nutritional demands.

Horses grow much faster than most owners realize. See below for a growth study of Quarter Horses at Louisiana State University. By six months of age the foals attained 44 percent of mature body weight. At twelve months the colts reached 58 percent, and at 24 months 87 percent of mature weight. In height, length, and heartgirth measurements they reached 95 percent at 18 months. This means the bone structure grew even faster than the rest of the body.

GROWTH DATA ON QUARTER HORSES *

	Males					(mature)
	Birth	6 mo.	12 mo.	18 mo.	24 mo.	60 mo.
Body weight (lb.)	102	526	694	976	1049	1201
Height (in.)	35.9	49.3	53.6	57.2	58.6	60.0
Length (in.)	26.8	47.6	53.9	57.7	61.1	61.9
Heartgirth (in.)	31.0	54.4	60.9	70.4	71.0	73.0
Elbow to ground (in.)	25.0	31.6	33.1	35.6	35.9	35.8
Knee to ground (in.)	14.5	17.9	17.8	17.9	18.3	18.0
Circumference cannon bone (in.)	4.5	6.3	6.9	7.5	7.5	7.9

	Females					(mature)
	Birth	6 mo.	12 mo.	18 mo.	24 mo.	60 mo.
Body weight (lb.)	97	512	733	905	949	1172
Height (in.)	35.7	49.5	53.7	55.8	56.4	58.3
Length (in.)	26.8	47.1	53.3	56.3	58.2	61.8
Heartgirth (in.)	30.4	54.7	62.3	67.4	69.1	72.3
Elbow to ground (in.)	24.4	31.9	33.3	34.6	34.0	34.8
Knee to ground (in.)	14.1	17.2	17.3	17.5	17.4	17.2
Circumference cannon bone (in.)	4.4	6.2	6.9	7.2	7.2	7.4

* Louisiana State University Experiment Station, Baton Rouge, La. (Cunningham and Fowler).

For proper bone growth and muscle development, protein, vitamins, and minerals are extremely important. And yet rations fed to growing horses often do not make an allowance for these extra needs. The recommended ration should contain 18 to 2o percent protein up to the yearling stage, and 13 to 15 percent for the yearling and two-year-old.

Legume hays, such as alfalfa, are higher in protein, vitamins, and minerals than grass hay, such as timothy. They are good for the growing horse. Calcium and phosphorus, major constituents of bone, generally are supplied by roughages and grains, or may be added as supplements.

NUTRIENT NEEDS FOR BREEDING

Reproduction results in additional nutrient requirements above maintenance. Most horse owners recognize this in the pregnant mare, but underestimate her needs when giving milk. Therefore, they tend to overfeed during pregnancy and underfeed during lactation.

Pregnancy does impose extra burdens on the mare, but not as much in terms of nutrition as many owners think. At birth the foal contains approximately 80 percent water. For example, with a 100-pound foal, the mare actually deposits only twenty pounds of energy, protein, vitamins, and minerals in the fetus in eleven months. Also, about 80 percent of the fetal growth occurs in the last four months. During the first six to seven months of pregnancy, the mare's requirements are barely more than maintenance.

Some breeders tend to get their mares too fat during pregnancy. This can cause foaling problems and subsequent breeding problems. Pregnant mares should be thrifty, neither overfat nor too thin. If a mare is thin and in poor health, she should be conditioned *before* breeding. In addition to energy nutrients, protein and vitamins are particularly important.

If the mare has foaled and is also producing milk, the situation is different (see below). A certain amount of body fat put on during pregnancy can be utilized during the lactation period.

The stallion's role in the breeding season is equivalent to hard work in terms of energy expenditure. Each spring, stallions in heavy service may be mated to 60 to 100 mares from February 1 to July 1, at the rate of one per day for six days out of each week. Occasionally as many as two or three services a day may be completed during four or five days. It should be no surprise that the stallion loses considerable weight.

Nutrition during the pre-breeding season is important for success. The stallion should put on some weight during the winter, but excessive fat will be detrimental. Protein, vitamins, and minerals are as essential as extra energy. The production and quality of sperm are greatly influenced by the ration. The horse should also be regularly exercised to bring him to a peak condition of health for the breeding season in the spring.

Feed a breeding stallion well in preparation for his heavy duties. It is good practice to feed a vitamin-mineral supplement during both the winter and the spring.

THE MARE AND HER MILK

Lactation, as noted above, puts a greater nutritional strain on the mare than most horse owners realize. Actually it is far greater than during pregnancy. To demonstrate this, we may use total digestible nutrients (TDN). A 1,000-pound mare in the last quarter of pregnancy will require 7.3 pounds of TDN per day. The same mare when suckling her foal requires 14.4 pounds of TDN, or nearly twice as much energy. Surely these are dramatic figures.

The reason is simple: the mare may produce as much as 32 to 42 pounds of milk per day. This is quite an accomplishment. Approximately 450 pounds of blood must circulate through the udder to produce one pound of milk—a tremendous amount of work. Milk production is at its peak at about the third month of lactation, then tapers off until the foal is weaned, at about six months of age.

Furthermore, a lactating mare is often a pregnant mare. A foal is born in the spring, then about one month later the mare is rebred. During the next six months, the extra nutritional needs of both reproduction and lactation are added to maintenance. But, to repeat, lactation is by far the bigger burden, and maximum growth of the foal will come only if this fact is understood by the feeder.

Don't overfeed during pregnancy. A maintenance ration of good quality feedstuffs is enough during the first six or seven months. Increase this slightly during the last quarter of pregnancy. Double the quantity for the nursing period, especially during the first months. In the ration, increase the proportion of concentrate or grain, since the mare cannot eat enough roughage to meet her lactating needs.

NEEDS OF THE WORKING HORSE

Work is usually associated in our mind with draft horses. Actually any man-made activity is "work" for a horse, whether it is a person riding for pleasure through Central Park in New York City, a 4-H'er showing his skill at an Iowa fair, or a cowboy riding herd in Texas. For modern thinking, we could substitute "performance" for work. The greater the work, the more energy feed needed. For light horses that are ridden or driven, the following work classes were set by the National Research Council in 1949:

> Up to 1 hour per day—maintenance
> 1 to 3 hours per day—light work
> 3 to 5 hours per day—medium work
> 5 to 8 hours per day—hard work

Since modern horses work at faster speeds than draft horses, requirement for work probably should be revised downward today in terms of hours. The light horse at fast speeds has a lower efficiency in converting feed to energy. He is also more nervous and this burns up energy.

To meet working needs, increase the concentrate or grain ration and decrease the roughage. The main mineral concern is sodium chloride, or salt, which is lost by sweating. A supplement of B vitamins may also be necessary, since these vitamins regulate the body reactions that produce energy.

In some situations work is so strenuous that the horse cannot eat enough to maintain body weight. This is not too serious so long as he is rested or put on lighter work until his weight returns to normal.

Chapter 10

Buyer's Guide to Common Feeds

Feeds for horses are normally classified by several scientific standards. A fault of the horse industry is ignoring these standards by feeding according to volume alone. The owner imagines that grain is grain—that feeding a quart of oats or a quart of corn makes no difference. In fact the corn weighs more per quart, and its energy content per pound is higher. Therefore, the quart of corn may give the horse twice as much energy as the same amount of oats.

Feeds are classified into various categories based upon their nutritional content. The first general grouping is based upon their fiber content and the total digestible nutrients (TDN) they supply. These two factors give an indication of the energy value of a feed. Concentrates are feeds low in fiber (18 percent or less) and high in TDN. Grains and grain by-products are in this group. Roughages are feeds high in fiber, more than 18 percent, thus low in TDN. Hay, straw, silage, and pasture are roughages. A further breakdown within each of these categories is based upon protein content. With concentrates, those of 16 percent protein or less are classed as basal feed, basically the grains. Those above this level, especially over 20 percent protein, are classed as protein supplements. Within roughages, protein content is not as exacting, but generally the legumes are higher in protein than the grasses. Stage of maturity is extremely important: an early-cut timothy hay, a non-legume, may have a higher protein content than a late-cut clover (legume).

Another term you should be familiar with is "ration"—the feed allowed for a given horse during a twenty-four hour day, whether fed at one or more feedings. A balanced ration furnishes the nutrients in amounts and proportions to properly nourish a horse for twenty-four hours. Total digestible nutrient represents an energy value of the feed, including

energy from carbohydrates, fats, and protein. The higher the TDN value, the higher the energy value of the feed. The percent protein refers to the digestible protein—that percentage which is absorbed and then hopefully utilized.

Because of the nature of the horse's digestive system a horse generally requires bulk, a volume-weight relationship. A bulky feed is one that has little weight for a given volume. A quart of oats normally weighs 1 pound while a quart of corn weighs 1.75 pounds. Oats are bulkier than corn. Because there is less weight, naturally there is less energy available. Roughages also supply bulk in the horse ration. The crude-fiber content indicates bulk, the higher the crude fiber the bulkier the feed.

This brings us to the consideration of weight per bushel. There is a standard weight per bushel for the grain. Oats are a standard 32 pounds per bushel. Horsemen prefer a heavier, plumper oat that weighs 40 or more pounds per bushel.

The good manager will think of two other considerations: the physiological requirements of the horse, and cost. Whether an animal is idle, working, breeding, or giving milk, determines the desirable ratio of energy, proteins, vitamins and minerals at any particular time. An owner with a sound knowledge of nutritional values can stretch his feed dollar farther while giving his horse better care.

The following table lists some of the more common horse feeds with their percentage TDN, protein, and crude fiber. The standard weight per bushel of the grain is also given.

NUTRITIVE VALUE OF COMMON HORSE FEEDS *

	Weight (lbs. per bushel)	TDN (percent)	Digestible Protein (percent)	Crude Fiber (percent)
Concentrates				
Oats	32	70	9.4	11
Barley	48	78	10	5.9
Corn	56	80	6.7	2.0
Milo	56	80	8.5	2.3
Wheat	60	80	11	2.6
Wheat Bran		67	13.3	10.0
Molasses	54		0	0
Linseed Oil Meal		76	31	8.9
Soybean Oil Meal		78	42	5.9
Cottonseed Oil Meal		73	34	10.5
Roughages				
Alfalfa Hay (very leafy)		53	12.8	22.7
Red Clover Hay (leafy)		55	9.2	23.3
Mixed Hay (30% more legume)		50	7.2	31.6
Timothy Hay (before bloom)		57	6.1	27.9
Prairie Hay (early-cut)		46	3.7	29.2
Bermuda Grass Hay (fertilized)		51	6.3	27.8
Bromegrass Hay (smooth before heading)		56	9.6	23.9
Bluegrass Hay, Kentucky		55	4.8	29.8

* Taken by permission of The Morrison Publishing Company, Clinton, Iowa, from the 22nd Edition, third printing, 1959, of *Feeds and Feeding* by F. B. Morrison and Associates.

CONCENTRATES

Oats. An old reliable among horse feeds, oats are palatable and horses love them. They are also safe. You can always feed oats successfully because they contain 30 percent hulls, or outer covering of the oat kernels, that give the ration plenty of bulk. Heavy feeds without much bulk, such as shelled corn, wheat, and vegetable oil meals, tend to form a packy, doughy mass in the stomach of the horse. Oat hulls, wheat bran, and the like prevent this difficulty; they keep the feed moving through the digestive system at a normal rate.

Nevertheless, oats are not the only good horse grain or even the most nutritious. Crimping the oats—a process of flattening the grain between metal rollers—increases nutritive value about 5 percent. Crimping is helpful particularly for horses with poor teeth, such as those 16 years of age or older, and the young foal less than eight months old. Otherwise the whole, unrolled oats are more economical.

Down through the ages, a standard ration for horses has been oats and timothy hay. This is sufficient for a mature animal doing very little work. Growing foals, mares in late pregnancy or lactating, and hard-working animals need more nutrients.

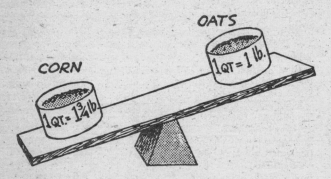

Barley. It is the predominant grain in many parts of Europe and Arabia. In this country it is used mostly on the West Coast and in the Midwest. Like oats, the barley grain has a hull around it, providing some bulk if it is the only grain fed. To increase bulk, a common practice is to mix in 10 or 15 percent wheat bran, or 25 percent oats. Either provides a good margin of safety.

Since the grain is quite hard, rolled or steamed rolled barley is recommended for easier chewing. This again is especially helpful with the older horse. Rolled barley has more bulk than the whole grains.

Do not be tempted to grind barley or other grains for horse feed. Coarsely ground grains are acceptable, but fine grinding lends itself to doughiness and digestive disturbances. Any grinding, coarse or fine, produces dustiness. As a rule, it's better to stick to the whole, crimped, or rolled grains.

Corn. For generations it was a common feed for draft horses in the Midwest and for mules in the Southeast. But having no hulls, it provides less bulk. Its high energy content, however, gives it advantages for strenuous performance animals.

Horsemen often complain that corn "heats a horse up." Obviously, since corn is rich in energy, feeding it in the same quantity as oats will fatten a horse. And in the summertime, a fat horse will produce more body heat. Just feed him less corn and more hay to lower the energy level in the summer.

Corn may be fed shelled or on the ear, but not ground. Steam rolling produces a flat kernel much like corn flakes and horses enjoy it. Another version is corn and cob meal made by grinding up the ears, corncob and all. Molasses is usually added to reduce dustiness. The cob adds bulk like the hulls of oats or barley. Corn is low in protein; therefore, it should be fed with a legume hay or protein supplement for brood-mares and growing horses.

Milo. Also known as sorghum grain, milo is grown in abundance in our Southwest and has been successfully used as a horse feed. It is a rather hard, round grain lacking in bulk. Steam rolling or crushing is necessary for easy chewing. Never grind milo because it tends to grind fine. Mix in bulkier feeds such as wheat bran, oats, or barley. Fed in large quantities by itself, milo tends to constipate.

Wheat. Because of its cost, wheat seldom is fed to horses. Nevertheless, in wheat-growing areas at the favorable season, it may be economically included in a ration. It is similar to corn as a high energy feed, but higher in protein.

Wheat should be rolled or crushed to make it easier to chew and digest. Very seldom is it fed in excess of 20 percent of the concentrate portion of a ration, and it must be mixed with bran, oats, or other bulky feed to prevent colic.

Wheat Bran. A by-product of milling, it is the coarse outer coating of the wheat kernel. Mixed with concentrates for adding bulk, it has a mild laxative effect. To make a bran mash, pour hot water over the dry bran and let it stand for 30 minutes or more. Add to the ration at least once a week, if it is not included in the daily ration.

Wheat bran should not exceed 10 or 15 percent of the concentrate ration. On non-working days, the proportion to feed is ⅔ normal grain, ⅓ bran.

Molasses. A popular component of mixed concentrates and a by-product of sugar refining, molasses is often a cheaper source of energy than common grains. Horses like the flavor and it has a mild laxative effect. It also helps to reduce dustiness in feed mixtures.

The proportion of molasses should not exceed more than 10 to 12 percent of the concentrate ration. Here is a simple way to check if enough molasses is in the ration: Pick up a handful of the mixture and tighten your fist as if holding a ball. When released, the feed should remain stuck together.

PROTEIN SUPPLEMENTS

The protein oil meals are by-products of extraction of seeds for their oil. Long considered the standard horse protein, *linseed meal* is produced from flax. Feeding this or other proteins induces bloom in the horse's coat.

Linseed meal should be fed with care as it may be too laxative. The rule of thumb is: no more than 1 to 1½ pounds per day.

As the table on page 105 shows, *soybean meal* is an even richer source of digestible protein than linseed meal. Usually it is cheaper per pound of digestible protein, and it contains a better balance of amino acids.

This is a heavy feed. Do not feed more than one pound per day. Soybean meal is an excellent protein supplement for broodmares, stallions, sucklings, and weanlings.

In our Southern cotton-growing states *cottonseed meal* offers a ready source of proteins. Again, this is a heavy feed. If eaten to excess it can cause digestive troubles even to the extent of becoming poisonous or toxic. Never feed more than 1 to 1½ pounds of it per day. Start the horse on a ¼ pound of cottonseed meal and gradually build up to the maximum amount. It's best to feed extra bulk, such as wheat bran or oats, at the same time.

COMMERCIAL FEEDS

Commercial feeds on the market are a combination of grains and grain by-products, proteins, added vitamins and minerals, and molasses to give them a sweet flavor. They are popular among horse owners as they seem to offer a complete answer to the nutritional problem, along with convenience and easy storage.

The protein content usually appears on the feed tag, along with fat, fiber, and sometimes calcium, phosphorus, or other minerals. The TDN is seldom stated, but we may arrive at an estimate of 73 to 75 percent from the values of commonly used feedstuffs. For most classes of horses, the nutritional levels are adequate, but the protein content may be too low for young, growing horses and lactating mares.

Cost should always be considered. These feeds may be reasonably priced for the owner with only one or two horses, but if you feed several horses, it may pay to work out your own formula with the local agriculture extension service. Most local feed mills can prepare a special mixture, with a possible savings of several hundred dollars a year.

A complete pelleted feed contains both grain and hay. It offers the advantages of convenience, less space for storage, and less dustiness. When hay is scarce or expensive, the pelleted feed may be a good buy, and it saves labor. Pelleted hay (without grain) has been shown to be preferred by the horse over baled hays. Consider these two factors: (1) the cost, which may be a high price for hay where the natural hays are plentiful; and (2) the quality of the hay used for pelleting.

One common problem with complete pelleted feeds is that the horse may tend to chew the wood on fences or in stalls. This is probably due to lack of bulk in the ration. It may also mean that the streamlined feed leaves him more time to acquire bad habits from boredom.

WHICH GRAIN SHOULD YOU FEED?

Your choice of grain depends mostly upon economics. Simply feed the cheapest source of energy that is also good for the horse. Use the following formula:

$$\frac{\text{Feed cost per 100 lbs.}}{\text{Percent TDN} \times 100} = \text{Cost per lb. of TDN}$$
(from table)

Fill in the following table using your own local feed prices which may change throughout the year. Then figure the cost per pound of TDN using the above formula.

FEED COST FOR ENERGY (TDN)

Feeds	Local Price per 100 lbs.	% TDN	Cost ¢ per lb. TDN
Oats, whole		70	
Oats, crimped		70	
Barley, crimped		78	
Corn, shelled		80	
Milo		80	
Wheat bran		67	
Molasses		54	
Soybean Meal		78	

As an example, let's assume the following prices for a few feeds. Plugging the feed cost into the formula, these are the costs per pound of TDN:

Feeds	Local Price per 100 lbs. (assumed)	% TDN	Cost ¢ per lb. TDN
Oats, crimped	$4.06	70	5.8
Barley, crimped	3.75	78	4.8
Corn	3.60	80	4.5
Molasses	2.16	54	4.0
Soybean Meal	5.65	78	4.1

No more than 12 percent of molasses should be used, so we put that down first. Since corn is lacking in bulk, we must mix in 25 percent of barley to provide bulk. If extra protein is required, add the cheapest source at the minimum level.

	Percent by weight
Molasses	12
Barley	25
Corn	63
	100

One hundred pounds of this concentrate mixture would provide 77 pounds of TDN at a cost of $3.48, while 100 pounds of crimped oats would provide only 70 pounds of TDN costing $4.06. Which is cheaper?

HOW TO SELECT ROUGHAGES

The roughage feeds include hay, pasture, silage, and straw. Straw, which is the stem of cereal grain plants cut at full maturity, is less efficiently utilized than hay and has so much less nutrient content that it should be considered only as bedding. Never feed straw to a horse.

A good hay provides bulk plus energy, protein, minerals, carotene, and several B vitamins. Despite the large proportion of bulk, hay is usually a cheaper source of energy than grains and should make up the major part of the ration for mature horses.

The higher the quality of hay, the greater the nutrient content. Look for green color, leafiness, and fine stems. These are the signs of early-cut hay. As the crop matures, the protein and energy (TDN) in it gradually decrease and the fiber content increases. Instinctively the horse prefers hay cut early to that cut in full bloom.

The smell or fragrance of clean, bright hay enhances its palatability and the horse will eat more of it. Never feed him moldy or dusty hay. For lack of a better roughage, the horse will eat it anyway. Mold or mustiness can give him colic, and dust can give him respiratory ills such as the heaves. (Sprinkle hay that is slightly dusty with a little water, or better still, avoid using it.)

If fed exclusively on good quality hay, the horse will eat about 2½ percent of his body weight per day. For example, the average 1,200-pound horse eats about 30 pounds of hay. This declines to 1½ percent of body weight when concentrates are also fed, or 18 pounds a day for the average horse. Under drought or similar conditions when hay prices skyrocket to $50 or $60 a ton, horses can do quite well on as little as 0.6 pounds of hay per 100 pounds of body weight. Replace the hay with extra grain at the rate of 1 pound of grain per 2 pounds of good quality hay, or per 3 pounds of fair quality hay. The 1,200-pound horse's ration could then be cut to as little as 7½ pounds of hay daily.

TYPES OF HAY

Legumes	Mixed	Grasses
Alfalfa	Legume and grass	Timothy
Red clover		Prairie hay
Other clovers		Orchard grass
		Bromegrass
		Bermuda grass
		Kentucky bluegrass

Legumes are plants of the pea family that produce seeds in a pod, take nitrogen from the air, and produce protein. Horses like them so well that they tend to overeat and this may cause colic. For this reason some horsemen avoid the legumes, but it should be clear that they can be extremely valuable for their protein. Mixed hays containing both legumes and grasses are a popular compromise.

The particular variety of hay is less important than the quality and the cost. The reasons ascribed for preferring one over the other often are more a matter of tradition than of science.

For many years timothy has been the standard horse hay, probably because it is relatively free from dust and mold. Horses like it. However, timothy is low in protein and minerals. If fed to broodmares or growing horses, it must be supplemented with protein.

Check the quality by the length of the head—about two inches when cut. At this stage timothy reaches its highest nutritive value.

Prairie hay is favored in the Western plains states. When of good quality it is good for horses, palatable, and usually free from dust and mold. Cut green, prairie hays are nutritionally very close to timothy. The same may be said of the other grass hays.

Alfalfa is a hotly debated subject in horse feeding. You'll find one horseman swearing by alfalfa hay and another horseman down the road swearing at it. Here are the facts: from a nutritional standpoint, legume hays are higher than grass hays in protein, vitamins, and minerals; therefore alfalfa hay is recommended for broodmares and young growing horses; but if fed without proper management, it can cause problems; in excessive amounts, it may lead to softness, heavy sweating, colic, loose bowels, and other digestive ailments.

A rule of thumb: don't feed more than 1 pound of alfalfa hay daily per 100 pounds of body weight, for example, 12 pounds per day for the average 1,200-pound horse. Make up the rest of the roughage ration with one of the good grass hays or a mixed hay. With careful management you can exceed this limit, but carefully observe your horses.

There is no evidence, incidentally, for the statement often heard that alfalfa hay can do harm to a horse's kidneys.

Mixed hays consist of legumes and grasses, usually alfalfa and timothy, or red clover and timothy. They are generally excellent feed for horses.

Most horse farms do not have silos, so silage is generally not used as a horse feed. Good corn or grass silage may be fed in limited amount as a substitute roughage for hay, and as an appetizer or tonic. It may replace from ⅓ to ½ the hay ration, but should not be the only roughage fed.

A rule of thumb: do not feed more than 10 to 15 pounds of silage daily. Because of the high moisture content, consider 3 pounds of silage equal to 1 pound of hay. For example, if a horse eats 15 pounds of hay per day, from 5 to 7½ pounds may be replaced by silage. Using the 3:1 ratio, the roughage could consist of 10 pounds of hay plus 15 (3 × 5) pounds of silage.

Start with small amounts to get the horse used to it. Inspect it carefully for quality. Moldy, decayed, or frozen silage should never be fed to horses.

PASTURE

By nature the horse eats grass and, to this day, pastures form the basis of horse production. In most situations, green forage eaten where it grows provides the cheapest, as well as a high quality of nutrition. The cost of pasturage has been estimated at one-half that of hay and one-fourth that of oats. On pasture, also, the horse gets exercise and sunshine, both important to his health. Young horses on pasture develop good feet and legs and stay healthy. Is is extremely important for broodmares and foals.

Grazing horses will clip the grass close to the ground before moving on. They tear up the turf with their feet, especially along fences or around watering and feeding areas. More pasture area is lost where the horses defecate; then they will not graze in the same spot. (But the droppings of cattle or other species do not bother them.) Not all grasses can stand this heavy traffic.

Kentucky bluegrass, the favorite horse pasture, has good turf-forming characteristics. But it should be mingled with other grasses. A rule of thumb: seed a mixture consisting of a good local legume, a local grass having strong seedling vigor, and Kentucky bluegrass.

The fertility of the soil decides not only how well the grass will grow but its nutrient value to the horse. Have the soil tested, then fertilize as recommended by your local agricultural university. Let the horses graze a field down to about two inches; then move them to another pasture while the first one has a chance to regrow. This is rotational grazing.

Overgrazing is a common problem. It simply indicates too many horses on too small an acreage. If pasture acreage is scanty, it is better to stable some of the horses, in turn, rather than see a good pasture lose all value. Sometimes the opposite problem occurs, especially in the spring. The plants grow too fast, they are not eaten down, and they become too mature, losing succulence. Clipping the pasture to a two-inch height (1) permits succulent regrowth; (2) helps maintain a balance of legumes with grasses; and (3) helps control weeds.

Chapter 11

The Art of Feeding Horses

Individuality in the feeding of horses counts more than with any other farm animal. Every horse is different. One may eat very slowly, seeming to take all day to put away his hay and grain, while a gluttonous stablemate bolts his feed. Some horses like their feed more moist than others do.

Study your horse to learn his temperament and habits, then feed him accordingly along with his nutrient and physiological needs. In other words, don't fight his habits—join them. This is good management. A combination of art and science will obtain maximum performance from the horse and save you money at the same time.

A horse is fed for work, in contrast to other farm animals that are fed for meat or milk production. Meat animals are fed for a short period of time. Lambs and pigs are marketed at five or six months and steers are slaughtered at about fifteen months. But a horse's span of useful work may extend to sixteen years or more.

We commonly consider a horse past ten years of age, called smooth-mouthed, to be past his prime. And yet with proper management, good nutrition and health care throughout life, the useful years can lengthen. Mares and stallions past twenty-six years have been known to produce offspring. Modern animal science and veterinary medicine have contributed much to longevity. The author knows of a mare who, although past thirty years of age, earns her own way as a school horse for a riding instructor. This mare has taught dozens of 4-H'ers and adults how to ride—naturally with a little assistance from the instructor.

The type of horse and the work he does must determine what and how much to feed. You would not give the same ration to a Man O' War as to Old Dobbin. Certainly an active horse will require more energy than an idle one.

A newly purchased horse, or one that has been sick, may often be too thin. In fact we use the expression, "off his feed," to describe an ailing animal. More grain in the ration usually will bring him around. Excess fat is also a serious matter, seen only too commonly today in pleasure horses that are kept idle too much of the time. If fed beyond maintenance needs all winter, come spring, this horse will be badly out of condition. Should you try to ride him, he could become seriously ill from the strain.

A nervous horse may be compared to a nervous man—he eats a lot but can't gain weight. A more placid individual eats sparingly and yet puts on fat. Racing breeds trained to high performance often are nervous eaters; so are some show horses.

Feeding on the ground is simple, but horses waste some hay, can pick up worm eggs, and can swallow sand or gravel.

It is important to emphasize once again the mistake of feeding on a volume basis. Most horsemen talk in terms of quarts and gallons and appear never to have heard of pounds. The wise owner will install a small, spring scale in the barn, or use a bathroom scale to weigh feed. Find out how many *pounds* of grain that old feed bucket or scoop really holds. Be sure to check this out whenever changing feed. Making changes without adjusting for weight of the new feed may lead to a case of colic. A general rule of thumb: a quart of oats = 1 pound, a quart of barley = 1.5 pounds, and a quart of shelled corn = 1.75 pounds.

The owner who feeds only one or two horses may pay little attention to cost. A feed selling for $4.00 per hundred pounds may not seem much more expensive than one selling for $3.50. Yet, for two horses over a period of a year, assuming 10 pounds of grain per day is fed each, the cheaper feed (if nutritionally adequate) would save $36.50. Good nutrition practices usually are good economics as well. The horse industry could save millions of dollars a year by feeding horses according to the principles given in this book.

Horsemen in certain areas commonly buy oats from other states, or from Canada, to obtain what they consider a proper horse oat. Locally grown grains, especially barley and corn, may be much cheaper and can be fed just as satisfactorily as the imported oats. The same applies to hay. Frequently timothy hay is shipped in at heavy transportation cost when alfalfa or good mixed hay is readily available locally at several dollars less per ton. It may even be better for the horse nutritionally. Consult your local agricultural extension agent or the state college of agriculture for money-saving advice on local feeds.

Lower cost should not be construed as lower quality. As stated before, horses are susceptible to digestive disturbances much more than other farm animals. Dustiness is a major problem, causing heaves and other respiratory ills. Legume hays are more prone to dust than grass hays, which is one reason for their unpopularity.

If hay is sprinkled with water to settle the dust, it should be fed immediately and discarded if not consumed by the end of the day. Otherwise mold may form. Ruthlessly discard a sack of grain with some moldy spots or a bale of hay that has been rained on and begins to spoil. This cannot be stressed too strongly. Always be selective about feeds, even downright fussy as to quality. There is no saving in a sick horse.

Some animals are quite difficult to feed. Those on the show circuit or in training may have to be pampered with four or five different feeds in rotation, in order to keep them doing well. Another horse may be satisfied with one diet and balk at any change.

Because of this individuality among horses, make all feed changes gradually—especially if you intend the change to be permanent. Take a week, or even longer. Feed habits are as ingrained in a horse as they are in a man. Suddenly switching feeds can upset a horse to the point where he won't eat, or he may even become seriously ill.

HOW TO FEED AN IDLE HORSE

Nowadays a large part of the horse population falls into the "idle" category: that is, he is ridden no more than one hour per day, or only on weekends. The weekend horse usually is out of condition and hard riding can hurt him.

The "Sunday rider" should keep his horse strictly on a maintenance ration of good quality roughage. Some owners who worry that this doesn't give the horse enough to eat, add some grain. But don't feed more than 2 or 3 pounds per day. As the amount of work increases—more pleasure riding, jumping, roping—the grain ration increases. A rule of thumb:

	Grain	Hay
	(per 100 pounds of body weight)	
Idle	0–¼	2–2½
Light work	½ lb.	1 to 1¼ lb.
Medium work	¾ to 1 lb.	1 to 1¼ lb.
Hard work	1¼ to 1½ lb.	1 to 1¼ lb.

The working horse also drinks more water. Make sure that enough salt is provided either in the ration or free choice.

HOW TO FEED A SHOW HORSE

Conditioning a horse for show or sale puts the owner's art of feeding to a real test. Many people put a lot of fat on the animal with the mistaken idea that it will improve his chance of winning or bringing a higher price. Actually any competent judge will know that extra fat is detrimental; he prefers good natural condition. A smart horse buyer knows that it takes several months to remove fat from a yearling before it can be placed in training. This is a waste of time and money. A horse in good show condition carries some fat, but he is not obese.

Accumulated fat causes a heavy cresty neck which is discredited in the show ring. Sweatbands or liniments used to remove fat would be unnecessary with proper nutrition and exercise. Extra fat also accumulates on the withers, making them muttony. Too much hay results in a grass belly, equally undesirable.

The good horseman treats his show horse as he would any horse in training for some performance event, such as racing. Don't just put him in a stall and feed high energy rations, without proper grooming and exercise. The show or sale horse does get extra feed, but along with riding, longeing, or ponying every day.

In preparing for a show, the problem is to get the horse to eat more concentrate. Gradually work him up to about 2 pounds of grain daily per 100 pounds of body weight. At the same time reduce the hay to about 1 pound per hundredweight. Feed him several times daily, or try different rations to tempt him. Proper exercise is as important as the ration.

HOW TO FEED A FOAL

The first six months of a horse's life, the suckling period from birth to weaning, are nutritionally vital. Weighing, on the average, 100 pounds at birth, the foal attains about 45 percent of mature weight during these first six months. With the emphasis today upon large size for early maturity, supplementary feeding is essential.

Most foals are born in the spring and weaned in the fall. The newborn foal *must* suckle the mare's first milk, called colostrum. It has a high vitamin content, is laxative, and contains antibodies that provide immunity against infections. It lasts about two days. After that, the mare reaches peak milk production at three months.

The foal will begin to nibble grain and hay at about one month, and may start as early as ten days old to nudge around in his mother's feed box. Encourage him to eat solid feed as soon as possible. A *creep* is a type of structure that allows foals to enter but keeps the mares out. It may be a shed or stall, built in the open. It is best located in an area of the pasture, near woods or a water hole, where the mares tend to loaf. Within this structure the grain (creep feed) is spread out in a thin layer in a trough.

In situations where mares and foals are stabled together, two other methods may be used: (1) let the foal eat with the mare—however, the mare will usually root him out and keep him from eating much grain; and (2) set up a separate feed box for the foal, tie the mare while the foal eats all he wants, then let the mare loose to clean up.

A good starter ration may be simply rolled oats, or rolled oats plus wheat bran, in a ratio of 4:1, sprinkled with brown sugar. Follow later with a mixture of oats, wheat bran, and soybean meal in a ratio of 4:3:1 or 5:4:1 by weight. Barley may be used in place of oats. In the first four or five weeks, try to get the suckling to eat about ½ pound of grain per 100 pounds of body weight. This builds up to about 1½ pounds daily for the three-month-old foal. By weaning time, the foal should be eating about ¾ of a pound per 100 pounds, equal to 3 or 4 pounds of concentrate per day.

Well managed, well fertilized pasture provides the best environment for raising foals. It's also economical. Where this is impossible or the pasture is poor, supplement both foal and mare with high quality legume hay.

WEANLING

The foal is a weanling between six months and one year of age—usually, that is, from the fall through the winter until the next spring. At weaning the young horse weighs about 520 pounds and will gain another 200 pounds over the winter. Again, this is a critical stage of development because of the rapid growth of bone, muscle and tissue.

Separating the foal from its dam is a hard and unhappy strain on both. Weaning should be well planned in order to prepare the foal and avoid any setback. The structure for weaning should be a familiar stall, shed, or pen. Carefully inspect it ahead of time for protruding objects, and remove or pad anything that might injure the panicky foal.

These steps will give best results:

1. Wean a group of foals at one time, as they tend to calm one another.

2. Move the mares completely away from the foals so they cannot be seen or heard.

3. Place an older, dry mare with the foals for a few days to give them comfort and companionship.

4. Prior to the actual weaning, get the foals accustomed to eating grain. This will help to offset the psychological shock of being separated from the mare and the milk supply of nutrients.

The weanling needs liberal amounts of protein, vitamins, and minerals along with adequate energy. Calcium and phosphorus in proper ratio, along with vitamin D, are vital for the rapid growth of bone. About a week or ten days after weaning, when the young animals have settled down, place them, if possible, on lush, well-fertilized pasture. For maximum growth, feeding of concentrates must continue. If pasture is unavailable or poor, feed excellent quality legume or mixed hay as a source of roughage.

Do the same through the winter months. Choose a concentrates mixture containing 18 to 20 percent protein, depending upon the quality and source of the roughage. In off-pasture periods, the recommended grain ration is 1 to 1½ pounds per 100 pounds of body weight. Recommended hay ration is 1½ to 2 pounds per hundredweight. Combine the lower limit of grain with the upper limit of roughage if good quality alfalfa or mixed hays are available; for example, 2 pounds of hay and 1 pound of grain.

The foal should also have a source of salt. A mineral mixture often fed to horses consists of one part salt and two parts dicalcium phosphate or steamed bone meal. A trough with two sections is a good idea, one containing salt only and the other this mineral mixture. The horse eats what he wants.

YEARLING AND TWO-YEAR-OLD

The yearling stage starts with the spring pasture, which can provide good growth without additional feeds. However, a common practice is to feed some extra grain, about ½ pound per 100 pounds bodyweight. If lacking a good pasture, give the yearling a full, dry-lot feed of concentrates, which would be about 1¼ to 1½ pounds of grain, plus about 1¼ to 1¾ pounds of hay per hundredweight body weight.

Going into the second winter, reduce the ratio to ½ to 1 pound of grain, 1 to 1½ pounds of hay, again per 100 pounds of bodyweight. Don't forget the salt and a mineral mixture if necessary.

The two-year-old needs more feed because of his increased size, but the same management given the yearling still applies. Good pasture during the third summer is adequate, followed by good grain and hay during the winter, the same schedule as for yearlings. He'll need more grain, however, for extra energy if he is being trained for racing. Feed 1½ to 2 pounds of grain plus 1 to 1½ pounds of hay per 100 pounds of weight. This will cover the combined requirements of maintenance, growth, and work.

HOW TO FEED A BROODMARE

Broodmares are pregnant mares that foal and are rebred in the spring. The length of pregnancy is approximately 340 days, or eleven months. As pointed out earlier, the mature broodmare requires sufficient feed for maintenance, for fetal development, and for extra heat increment due to an increase in the metabolic rate during pregnancy. If the mare is being ridden more than one hour a day, she has a work requirement as well.

Up until the last four months of pregnancy, development of the fetus is slow. A good maintenance ration will suffice unless much riding is being done. Good pasture will provide this ration, but if the pasture is poor, feed the mare about ¾ to 1½ pounds of grain a day per 100 pounds of weight. Continue at the same level during the last four months, the most critical period. You can let broodmares consume all the hay they want, except a straight legume hay, which should be restricted to 1 pound per 100 pounds. Provide salt and a mineral supplement if necessary.

Another vital consideration in feeding a broodmare is lactation. The mare nursing a foal is a heavier milker than generally realized (about 32 to 42 pounds per day), especially during the first three months. This is the requirement for maintenance, the heat increment of lactation, plus the nutrients required to produce the milk. She is usually on pasture, which cannot possibly meet all her requirements. Supplement her with 1 to 1½ pounds of grain daily per 100 pounds of body weight and with an equal amount of good quality hay if the pasture is poor. Feeding extra vitamins may also be advisable. After weaning, a maintenance ration will be adequate until about four months before foaling again. Then resume the pregnancy cycle described above.

Salt should be iodized for a lactating mare if the area is known to be deficient in iodine. The mineral mixture given to foals (salt and dicalcium phosphate or steamed bone meal) is good also for the mare.

FEEDING HINTS

1. Feed each horse as an individual; study the horse to know his feeding habits.
2. Consider all of these factors: age, type of performance, condition, and temperament.
3. Feed by weight, not by volume.
4. Feed two or three times a day if possible. Divide the grain portion of the ration equally among the feedings. Feed the larger portion of hay at night; in twice-a-day feeding: one-third morning and two-thirds evening; and for three daily feedings: one-fourth, one-fourth, and one-half morning, noon, and evening.
5. Feed at the same time each day.
6. Make ration changes gradually.
7. Feed only quality grains and hays; never feed dusty, moldy, or spoiled feedstuffs.
8. A well-managed pasture is the basis of good horse production; it supplies quality nutrients at economical cost.
9. Build the ration around a good quality hay that is the most economical for the class of horses being fed.
10. Purchase the grain on the basis of the cheapest source of energy. Also, purchase protein on the basis of cost per pound of digestible protein.
11. In the case of expensive hay, reduce amount fed and increase the grain portion of ration.
12. Always provide an abundant supply of clean, fresh water.
13. Provide adequate exericise.
14. Do not overfeed horses or allow them to become extremely fat.
15. Keep the feed box clean; never allow old, moldy, or spoiled feed to accumulate.
16. Decrease grain allowance on idle days, or as work decreases. Increase it when work increases.
17. Don't feed more than 1 pound of alfalfa hay per 100 pounds body weight.
18. Horses will consume about 2½ percent of their body weight in feed.
19. Always provide a source of salt.

FEEDING FORMULAS

Suckling (Creep Feed)	% by weight
(1) Oats (crimped)	50
Cracked corn	15
Wheat bran	15
Soybean meal	20
(2) Steamed rolled oats	70
Soybean meal	11
Wheat bran	10
Molasses	7
Steamed bone meal	1
Iodized salt	1

Weanling

(1) Milo, crushed	35
Oats, rolled	20
Cottonseed meal	10
Chopped alfalfa	25
Molasses	10
(2) Steamed rolled oats	27
Steamed rolled barley	26
Steamed rolled corn	20
Soybean meal	15
Molasses	10
Steamed bone meal	1
Iodized salt	1

Yearling

(1) Barley	40
Oats	23
Wheat bran	10
Soybean meal	15
Molasses	10
Steamed bone meal	1
Iodized salt	1
(2) Steamed rolled oats	54
Steamed rolled barley	20
Cracked yellow corn	10
Wheat bran	10
Soybean meal	5
Steamed bone meal	0.5
Trace mineralized salt	0.5

Two-year-old
(1) Oats 50
    Wheat bran 15
    Molasses 12
    Soybean meal 23

Pregnant mare	Early	Late
(1) Barley	50	40
Oats	30	30
Soybean meal	11	11
Molasses	7	7
Wheat bran	—	10
Steamed bone meal	1	1
Iodized salt	1	1

Lactating mare
(1) Barley 30
    Oats 30
    Corn 10
    Soybean meal 11
    Wheat bran 10
    Molasses 7
    Steamed bone meal . 1
    Iodized salt 1

Stallion	Breeding	Non-breeding
(1) Corn	10	—
Oats	30	45
Barley	36	35
Soybean meal	15	11
Molasses	7	7
Steamed bone meal	1	1
Iodized salt	1	1

Safeguards for Your Horse's Health

To obtain maximum pleasure and performance from a horse, he must be in good health and physically fit. It is imperative, therefore, that a horse owner establish a health and sanitation program to provide maximum protection and care for his horse.

Usually it is easy to tell when a horse becomes ill. The healthy animal is alert and inquisitive, without being nervous. When a horse stands with head down and ears drooped, things are not right. His eyes should be bright, clear, and glistening, not dull, grayish, or partly closed. He should have an easy, free way of moving and stand on all four feet (except when resting a hind foot by standing on three feet, which is normal).

Horses love to eat, so when a horse goes "off his feed," look out. You should be prepared to check further by taking his temperature and pulse. A horse can run a fever just as people do. Any deviation in his heartbeat and rate of breathing can be a sign of sickness.

HOW TO TAKE TEMPERATURE AND PULSE

Every horseman should own an animal thermometer (rectal) of rugged construction. Your horse will always feel a bit warm to the touch, since his normal body temperature, about 100 degrees Fahrenheit, is a couple of degrees higher than yours; also, it rises with exercise or excitement. Foals may have a temperature of 102 degrees, especially on hot, humid days. But if your horse feels hot without good reason, or refuses to eat, take his temperature.

Lubricate the thermometer with petroleum jelly, and insert it into the anus. Tie a string to the end of the thermometer and attach a paper clip on the other end of the string.

This allows you to fasten the clip to some of the tail hairs or hairs on the body so you cannot lose the thermometer. Some horses will clamp their tail down, making it impossible for you to hold the thermometer. Others may kick, if you attempt to hold their tail out of the way. This is a safe, easy solution to the problem. Leave it inside the rectum for three minutes; report the reading to the veterinarian.

Also, take the horse's pulse. His heart beats just about half as fast as your own, averaging 36 to 40 beats per minute. You can feel the pulse under either side of the jaw where a large artery passes. Press the artery gently with the second finger, count the beats for fifteen seconds, then multiply by four. Some horses are not used to having their heads fooled with and become excited, which results in an increase in the pulse rate to about 60. Waiting for about one minute will return it to normal. Another good place for pulse-taking is an artery high on the inside of the foreleg near the elbow joint. Since the rate may range—from 28 in sleep to 42 after exercise, excitement, and ordinary digestion—experiment with your horse at different times to get an idea of his average pulse.

Count his respiratory (breathing) rate by watching the rise and fall of the ribs or rear flank. Each rise and fall constitutes one breath; there should be eight to twelve breaths per minute in a mature horse at rest. Yearlings and two-year-olds breathe a little faster (10 to 15 per minute).

Some other signs to look for: a healthy horse has a glossy coat and the skin is movable, if one grasps it gently. A heavy, rough winter coat also is natural. The mucous membrane linings of the eye, nostrils, and mouth reveal the character of the circulating blood. A paleness indicates congestion of blood in other areas, or general blood deficiency. Excessive redness indicates inflammation. Yellowish color indicates that the liver may be affected. Dry membranes indicate a fever. Changes from normal in urine or manure may also be signals of illness.

A good horseman will be a good observer. Don't be like those who say, when their horse strains and dribbles urine, "My horse has kidney trouble." Scientifically speaking, this is nonsense. Horses rarely suffer from kidney disease. Most likely the horse strains because of colic. Better to tell the veterinarian exactly what occurs, without hazarding diagnostic guesses.

HYGIENE

When we hear the word sanitation, cleanliness comes immediately to mind. Keeping clean is part of a sanitation program, but only a part. The word really includes *all* of the conditions favorable to health. With horses, that means feeding, clean facilities and equipment, grooming, and exercise as well as hygiene and preventive medicine.

If your horse is fed a balanced ration, enjoys clean shelter and equipment, good pasture, and your good right arm with a brush to promote his bloom, then you already have a sanitation program well under way. Some tips on preventing disease, on keeping your horse healthy and happy, and on taking care of his minor injuries, are given in this chapter.

The diseases that call for veterinary help are described on pages 139-147.

The germs that cause equine diseases readily pass from one horse to another. Sometimes they pass by direct contact, or through the air; more often a healthy horse picks up the "bugs" from a water trough, manger, or stall that a sick horse has previously used. To break the chain of contact, the owner must either change the equipment or disinfect it.

A disinfectant is a chemical agent that kills the microorganisms causing disease. It is not the same as an antiseptic, which inhibits the growth and reproduction of germs but does not kill them. Most disinfectants are too toxic to use on the body; they are applied on walls, floors, or equipment. Antiseptics are used on living tissue, as in the treatment of wounds. A good disinfectant also acts to remove dirt and grease, and to deodorize the area.

Begin your health program the day a new horse arrives at the farm. He must be isolated from all other horses for at least three weeks, to make sure he is not harboring any disease. Provide quarters away from the main stable or barn, perhaps with a neighbor who has cattle but no horses. Prevent access to a pasture used by the other horses, or even to an adjacent pasture. (The horses will rub noses over the fence, to get acquainted.) The author has seen an isolation program destroyed by carelessness in dumping the bedding of the isolated horse in the regular pasture. Isolation means *isolating*— no contact at all, direct or indirect. Use separate feeding and watering equipment.

During the three weeks observe the new horse carefully
for any signs of sickness. Have the veterinarian check it and
give the horse the routine immunization shots and treat for
parasites. After releasing the horse, clean and disinfect the
isolation stall thoroughly. Handle any horse that has been sick
in the same way. After transporting a horse anywhere, clean
and disinfect the vehicle and carefully dispose of the bedding. The moving about of horses for shows, trail rides, and
races gives diseases the opportunity to spread. Many owners
give a horse an antibiotic, penicillin-streptomycin, shot *before*
shipping.

Insects and rodents should be controlled, as they may
carry diseases. Sound hygiene becomes especially important
on breeding farms. For example, stud farms may insist upon
a health certificate, *except* for a mare with a foal at her side.
Actually one cannot assume that such a mare is free from infection. A mare with a foal may have an infection just as easily as an open or barren mare.

Infection in the mare's reproductive tract occurs more frequently than most horse owners realize. "Windsuckers,"
usually found in older mares, tears or bruises in the vagina
caused during foaling, may result in infection. Unclean hands,
or instruments used during the breeding or foaling process
may also cause infection. Mares with infections are difficult
to get in foal. If such infected mares are bred and the
stallion is not properly washed, the infection may be spread
to other mares.

All mares should be examined for infections before breeding: (1) the vagina can be examined, with a speculum, for
white or yellowish fluid (pus) on its floor and an excessive
red color; (2) a smear of the cervix can be taken and cultured
to determine what bacteria, if any, are present. This leads to
positive identification of an infection and its causative agent,
which tells the veterinarian the specific treatment required.

The common infections of mares are *Staphylococci, Strepto-
cocci, Bacterium coli* and *Pseudomonas aeruginosa.*

In the case of "wind-suckers," a Caslick's operation can
be performed. This consists of closing the vulva by suturing it
from the top down. The location of the last suture depends
upon the individual case. The sutures are normally removed
in 10 to 12 days, when that area of the vulva has grown together. This operation, quite common today, will prevent

feces and wind from being sucked into the vagina, thus eliminating the source of the infection.

Other hygiene practices with mares are these:

1. Isolate visiting mares from the farm mares.

2. Provide adequate care and management, especially a balanced ration, regular exercise, parasite control, and proper grooming.

3. Wrap the mare's tail with a clean bandage before breeding.

4. Wash and thoroughly rinse the vulva and hindquarters of the mare before breeding.

5. Don't use the practice of splashing a bucket of (usually cold) water on the rearquarters of the mare to make her retain the semen; this practice not only may frighten the mare, resulting in serious injury to her and the handler, but it absolutely does no good. Walking the mare immediately after breeding, keeping her from straining and urinating, is much more beneficial.

A good stud farm usually isolates its stallions from the other horses. The feeding, exercising, grooming, health and parasite programs of the stallion are extremely important. In grooming, the underline of the stallion should be kept clean. This prevents dirt and hair from being carried into the reproductive tract of the mare.

During the breeding season the sheath and genital should be washed with warm water and castile soap before and after each service. Thorough rinsing is necessary to remove all soap. A mild disinfectant may be used in washing after the service. Most stallions have to be trained for this procedure. During the non-breeding season periodic washing is necessary to prevent smegma. (See page 138 for a discussion of this.)

PREVENTIVE MEDICINE

It is always much easier to prevent a disease than to cure one, and it costs much less. Giving a horse an antibiotic before shipping him certainly is better than having him bring back distemper. A new vaccine against strangles should also be widely used in this situation. Here are some other preventive steps to be worked out with your veterinarian:

1. *Tetanus shots.* If the horse has already been immunized with the series of two shots, an annual booster is all that is

required. It is always advisable to give a tetanus shot to get immediate protection.

2. *Sleeping sickness.* Where equine encephalomyelitis (sleeping sickness) is known to exist, annual immunization should be given as two injections at seven-day intervals in late spring and early summer. The annual tetanus booster may be given at the same time.

3. *Virus abortion.* A spray series is given to broodmares if needed (see Chapter 14) to prevent a disease that causes loss of the foal. Once started, the vaccine program is required annually since the virus has been introduced onto the property.

4. *Parasite control.* See Chapter 14 for details; what's important is a *regular* program. Combatting parasites requires at least two treatments per year for mature horses, and more for young horses.

5. *Teeth.* Horses, like people, should have an annual dental checkup. Checking the teeth is especially important with young horses and with old ones.

6. *Feet.* Clean the feet of a stabled horse every day (see Chapter 8). All horses need to have their feet checked regularly and trimmed, if necessary.

7. *Wounds.* Since a wound can always be a source of infection, prompt treatment is preventive medicine. Methods of treatment follow in this chapter. Also, remove from pastures and stalls old machinery, rusty wire, or anything that may cause injury.

8. *Grooming and exercise.* Once more, we can only repeat that good grooming and regular exercise are an extremely important phase of health care of the horse.

9. *Careful observer.* Keep a keen eye on your horse at all times, consulting your veterinarian at the first sign of major trouble. Make a complete list of symptoms, which will help him in making an accurate diagnosis.

FIRST AID

A horse, like an active child, is prone to injury. Wounds occur every day, but fortunately many of them are not serious. However, the natural instinct of a horse is to run when frightened. He is, thus, apt to run when caught in wire, or the like, and can injure himself badly. Sometimes he will lie down against a wall and be unable to get up; then he is said to be "cast." He tries to kick himself free, with unhappy consequences.

Most such accidents can be prevented by good management and care of facilities. But accidents do happen. If they seem serious or if there are complications, don't hesitate to call the veterinarian. Many of the minor wounds require only first aid, but horses' wounds need prompt treatment more than those of other domestic animals.

WOUNDS

There are five classes of wounds: bruise, abrasion, incised, laceration, and puncture.

Bruise. This is any surface injury that does not break the skin. Common causes are kicks, falls, or other trauma. Bleeding under the skin causes swelling, along with fluid, and discoloration, like a black eye—except that the darkening is invisible because of the horse's dark skin. Small bruises should be left alone; in a few days the blood will be reabsorbed and the swelling will go down.

Larger bruise, called a blood blister (hematoma), may take longer, and in some cases may have to be lanced and drained. This should not be done for a few days to insure that all bleeding has ceased, because hemorrhage might result and be difficult to stop.

Abrasion. This is a scrape of the skin caused by a rope burn or rubbing against a trailer wall. It may bleed a little and ooze a fluid; it hurts and will heal rather slowly. Clean the abrasion with a saline solution and soap; apply an antiseptic or antibiotic ointment. This keeps the scab soft to promote healing. If the wound becomes infected, the veterinarian should be called.

Incised. This wound is a clean cut, such as that made with a sharp knife, the edge of a sheet of tin or broken glass. The principal danger is excessive bleeding. Tissue damage is usually minimal. A pad and bandage over the wound will usually stop the bleeding. Apply an antiseptic ointment as above. A tourniquet is necessary only if a large vessel is severed; it should be loosened hourly to provide blood to the tissues.

Laceration. It is a cut with torn, irregular edges, the kind a horse gets from struggling to free himself from barbed wire. This is the common "cut" observed by horse owners. A tear does not bleed as much as an incision, but healing is slow. The tissue is usually damaged extensively and there is great danger of infection. Treatment is similar for incised wounds and lacerations. Mistreatment results in exuberant granulation (proud flesh), excessive scarring, blemishes, and maybe even unsoundness. Important factors in the treatment of wounds are control of hemorrhaging (bleeding), cleanliness, and drainage. Avoid over-treatment with agents that cause the wound to become dry, cracked, or overstimulate the injured tissue during healing. Cleaning the wound is extremely important and must be done carefully and completely. Shave all the hair about half an inch all around the wound. Hairs that get into the wound may irritate it and result in proud flesh. Flush out the wound with a warm saline solution. Do not swab; it may wipe away healing cells. Remove all dirt, hair, and dead tissue from the wound, then apply an antiseptic ointment. Smear the hairs below the wound with petroleum jelly or ointment. As the wound drains, this will prevent the discharge from sticking to the hair and irritating the skin.

Only nature can heal a wound; man must work with nature and avoid hindering the healing process. Certain wound dressings such as iodine, metaphen, merthiolate, oil base preparations and powders may irritate the tissue and cause more harm than good. A good wound dressing should keep the wound moist, rather than dry, and aid in the natural healing process.

A principal concern is the danger of proud flesh, which is uncontrolled tissue growth. If this occurs while the wound heals, the edges of the skin do not come together evenly, and the tissue grows outward. Hairs getting into the wound can cause this (which is why you shaved off the nearby hair); also, movement in the area of the wound and a lack of pressure may prevent the joining of skin edges evenly. These are the reasons that this condition is commonly seen on the legs.

The decision to suture a wound should be left to your veterinarian; wounds should be sutured, if possible, but certain types of wounds in certain locations do not suture well. In deep tears, where the deeper tissue damaged will slough off, suturing is normally not beneficial. Wounds of the face, those below the knees and hocks or over a bony area usually are sutured. In other areas they are not sutured because inflammatory swelling and movement will cause sutures to pull out.

Sometimes, wounds are sutured even though they will be pulled out to set the injured tissue for more rapid healing. The main reason wounds over bony areas are sutured is to reduce the chance of proud flesh.

Puncture. A puncture wound usually results from a nail in the foot or a splinter in other parts of the body. The outside of a deep wound tends to heal ahead of the inside—a perfect environment for tetanus microorganisms. Dirt, manure, and other foreign material collect in these wounds. The opening should be properly cleaned, shaved, and enlarged to provide drainage. Tetanus antitoxin is a must, antiphlogistic (heat-producing) paste or magnesium sulfate will reduce the swelling.

Puncture wounds of the foot are common. Do not remove the nail until the opening has been sufficiently enlarged for drainage, so it can be found. Hydrogen peroxide or an enzyme preparation can be used to clean the wound. It may be packed with iodine or anti-inflammatory ointment paste; bandage it as protection against moisture and filth. Tetanus antitoxin should be given at once. If the nail is a long one, it could penetrate into delicate parts of the foot, calling for extensive treatment to prevent lameness.

SPRAINS AND STRAINS

Any horse that runs or jumps can twist his foot or pull too hard on a joint. This can cause an injury which stretches or slightly tears the ligaments around the joint which, while not damaging the bone, causes swelling and pain. Overextensions, sudden stops and movements can bring on these conditions which respond to rest, cold applications to remove inflammation and then hot applications with massage.

INFLAMMATION—NATURE'S WAY OF HEALING

When there is some irritation in the body, inflammation occurs; it is characterized by pain, heat, and swelling. The first symptom observed is pain, which serves two purposes. It prevents movement of the joint and it stimulates blood circulation to the affected area. The arteries to the area increase in size to accommodate the increased blood flow. The veins cannot carry the blood away from the wound as fast as the arteries bring it; therefore, swelling occurs due to the blood plasma, which is forced through the capillary walls into the injured tissue area. This increased blood supply produces the two other facets of inflammation—heat and swelling. The inflammation process can correct many conditions by itself; however, in some cases infection may be a complicating factor. Since healing may take some time, the horseman tries to speed it up with various treatments.

A cold application counteracts the inflammation and reduces or prevents swelling. Cold applications result in constriction of blood vessels, which reduces the blood flow to the area, and the applications also produce a decreased tissue metabolism, reducing the exchange of material between the blood and the tissue. The ice pack or cold-water bandage must be applied immediately; it will do no good a few days after the initial sprain.

A heat application has the opposite effect: it increases the blood flow, the exchange between the blood and tissue, and stimulates the activity of the white cells to fight infection. In combination with massage and liniment, it is used to good effect as a follow-up to cold packs, and in cases of chronic inflammation or infection.

Massage is an aid to the cold and hot applications. It helps to increase the circulation of blood during and after hot applications and assists in the removal of swelling.

Poultices are soothing applications since their moisture and warmth favor the development of putrefactive and infective microbes. The end result is an abscess which comes to a head, ruptures, and thus drains away the infectious material. Poultices are made of flax seed, bran, and oatmeal, and are held in place by bandages.

Liniments are liquid materials that produce a mild irritation. They are applied by massage, three to five minutes, which helps increase blood circulation. Liniments are useful for muscle soreness, sprains, and strains. They are normally used—after strenuous exercise or transportation—on horse's legs and muscles, to help prevent and relieve muscle soreness. Some contain drugs that relieve local pain.

Blistering or scuffing agents, increasing the normal shedding of skin, are irritants which cause an accumulation of fluids between the layers of skin; the outer layer dies, sloughing away, a scuff is produced, and a new layer formed. These agents are used to treat unsoundness. The hair is clipped and petroleum jelly is used to protect adjacent areas which are not to be blistered. A blistering agent may be a liquid commonly called "paint" or an ointment that is rubbed into the skin. Paints produce mild to medium blisters and contain drugs like iodine, mercuric chloride, or sodium iodide in an alcoholic solution. The ointments produce a severe blister and may contain red iodine of mercury, cantharides, or a combination of the two. Severe blistering and firing may cause pain. The horse should be restrained and kept under close observation to prevent injury.

Firing. This is an even stronger counterirritant, used for treatment of bone trouble such as splints, ringbone, and osselets. The veterinarian applies a hot iron with sharp points that barely pierce the skin. This causes a local inflammation, and besides the healing of an increased blood supply, it promotes the growth of fibrous tissue to strengthen the area. Although there is a difference of opinion as to the merits of firing, it does force the horse to rest. Firing and severe blistering should be done by a veterinarian.

Scratches are seen behind the fetlock and heel as red, tender skin that exudes a greasy material, known as "greasy heel" when severe, or they appear as masses of proud flesh ("grapes"). Scratches occur most often in the hind feet, caused usually by standing in snow, slush, or mud, especially if the fetlock is hairy. Good grooming, including clipping the long hairs, and properly dry facilities should prevent scratches.

Thrush. Thrush is an infection of the frog of the horse's foot. Signs of thrush are an offensive odor and a discharge of black necrotic material from the center and sides of the frogs. Pressure on the frog usually reveals soft areas with this discharge. The disease may penetrate to the sensitive portions of the hoof and result in lameness. The frog may be so infected that it is shed and a new frog grown.

It is caused by unsanitary conditions. Dirty, unclean feet, and a lack of frog pressure are predisposing conditions to thrush. *Spherophorus necrophorus* is the most important organism involved in this disease. It is most prevalent with horses in tie stalls where they stand in manure- and urine-soaked bedding.

Treatment consists first of removing the cause—unsanitary conditions—by keeping the stalls dry and clean. Medications such as tincture of iodine, one part phenol to one part iodine, 10 percent formalin and 10 to 15 percent sodium sulfapyridine solution, are usually required in severe cases to destroy the microorganisms which deteriorate the frog.

Prevention is the best avenue of attack by (1) thoroughly cleaning and examining the feet of stabled horses daily, (2) keeping stalls (box or tie) clean and dry, and (3) providing proper drainage in all stalls.

Smegma. Smegma is an accumulation of dried, hardened fatty secretions of the sheath and genitals of stallions and geldings. Commonly called a "bean," it may shut off the urinary passageway, resulting in the horse's straining in an effort to urinate. In addition to straining, the sheath is enlarged. Periodically the sheath and genitals of the male should be washed to remove this material. (See page 131.)

Chapter 13

Diseases and How to Recognize Them

For a horse owner to do an effective and efficient job of caring for his horse, he must have a general understanding of the more common horse diseases. This chapter is not intended to be a do-it-yourself medical guide. The symptoms of several diseases are much alike; only a trained veterinarian can tell them apart. Beware, also, of folk medicine in treating horses; many tales you still hear have been exploded as false. If your horse shows symptoms of pain, has been severely cut or bruised, or acts abnormally in any way, you should call the veterinarian at once.

You can (1) take and report the temperature; (2) become a careful observer and report all changes in your horse's action and your management program; and (3) keep your horse as comfortable and as calm as possible until the veterinarian arrives.

COLIC OR ABDOMINAL PAIN

Colic, a rather general term referring to pain caused by some form of a digestive disorder, is the ailment most likely to affect all horses at one time or another. It can come on suddenly and very violently, often leading to complications that may cause death. Every owner should have a colic remedy to be administered as his veterinarian directs. Speedy treatment is of the essence.

There are then two categories of colic: true colic and false colic. False colic is pain caused by some pathological or other condition outside of the digestive tract. True colic is pain originating from a digestive disturbance. This discussion will relate only to true colic.

The horse suffering from colic is very restless and will not eat. He paws the ground, stamps his feet, kicks at the painful abdomen, turns his head to look at it. He may lie down or roll over. He will break out in a sweat, will groan, stretch and strain in an attempt to urinate or defecate. With severe pain, the horse may drop to the ground as if shot. He thrashes around violently. His head may become so beaten and bruised that the eyes are swollen shut. His pulse and respiratory rates increase, but temperature may remain normal.

The causes of pain are various. With an *inflammation* of the stomach or intestine, the horse commonly has diarrhea. He may switch his tail, draw a rear leg up to the stomach, look anxiously at the rearquarter. Generally, an inflammation may be traced to improper feeding and management, less often to parasites or an infectious disease.

An acute *dilation* of the stomach is caused by excessive consumption of feed or water, impaction, and gas. The horse appears badly bloated. He sweats profusely, kicks, breathes rapidly, and may sit on the haunches with forelegs extended like a dog. He may try to vomit. Dilation of the stomach is an exceedingly dangerous condition, but the horse that can survive for four days will most likely live.

The gas usually comes from fermenting, spoiled feeds. Also, horses with the bad habit of cribbing (grasping the manger) often swallow too much air. The sick horse should be kept walking until the veterinarian arrives.

Good feeding practices and management are the most important preventive measures. Feeding excess grain, highly fermentable feeds, grains which form doughy masses, and sudden changes in the type or amount of feed are to be avoided. Horses should not be exercised immediately after eating. After exercise, allow only a limited water intake until your horse has been properly cooled out.

An *impaction* is severe constipation caused by a blockage of the large intestine, with a mass of ingesta. Again, bad feed is the chief villain, especially coarse roughages. Overeating of legume hays, poor chewing, especially of roughages, limited water intake, and lack of exercise are also responsible for impaction. In the Southwest, especially in drought years, horses got sand colic from picking up sand while grazing. Unless the plugging can be quickly relieved, the animal will be in a bad way. It is most severe if it occurs in the small colon; relief is required within 24 hours, if the horse is to be helped.

Often a horse tumbles about so violently that he causes an obstruction, called "*twisted gut.*" It occurs in two forms: (1) torsion, in which the intestine becomes twisted on itself or bent, as a garden hose sharply bent will block the flow of water; (2) intussusception or a telescoping of the intestine. Surgery offers the only hope, with a torsion, and the chances are poor. Smooth-muscle relaxants and the introduction of large volumes of water and enemas have been successful to some degree.

Parasites, too, can cause inflammation of the digestive tract and colic. The real problem is the bloodworm, *Strongylus vulgaris*, which often disrupts the blood supply, and thus the nutrients, to the intestinal tract. This results in an unhealthy, weak tract which is predisposed to colic. In extreme cases a portion of the intestine may become devitalized, and cause death.

WHAT TO DO ABOUT COLIC

At the first signs, call your veterinarian. Do not wait to call him until it is too late. Follow his instructions to administer any emergency remedies. Until he arrives, keep the horse moving, if possible. If he is cool or cold, blanket him. Walk him around to release gas.

Quite obviously, though, most cases of colic can be prevented by good stable management. Follow these rules to protect your horse:

1. Feed good quality hays and grains that are free from dust and mold.
2. Make ration changes slowly.
3. Have and keep to a sound feeding routine.
4. Supply plenty of clean, fresh water at all times.
5. Give the horse sufficient exercise to keep him thrifty.
6. Have your horse's teeth checked annually.
7. Follow a definite parasite prevention and control program.
8. Keep emergency remedies on hand as recommended by your veterinarian.

COLDS AND THE "FLU"

Horses are peculiarly susceptible to respiratory diseases, ranging from a mild distemper to the virtually incurable heaves. The symptoms are quite similar to human sniffles: a runny nose, cough, loss of appetite, and fever. A horse usually catches a "bug" from other horses at shows, sales, or racetracks; from using a common water trough, bucket, or manger. Direct contact is not always needed to get a viral infection.

Equine distemper has acquired the common name of shipping fever because of its prevalence among transported horses, but is more accurately termed *strangles*. It is a bacterial disease which is contagious. It is an infection of the respiratory system and invades the lymph nodes. Horses usually have a temperature of 104 to 106 degrees Fahrenheit and increased breathing. Depression, loss of appetite, a nasal discharge after the second or third day are other symptoms.

One sign of strangles is the swelling of lymph glands on the neck and under the jaw. Swellings may abscess and abscesses should never be lanced until one can easily pull out a few hairs; this indicates that rupture is near anyway and reduces the chance of spreading the disease to other parts of the horse's body. Less than 2 percent of strangles cases are fatal. Sick horses require good nursing; avoid stress and provide a draft-free, well-bedded stall with water at all times.

A vaccination program requires two weeks, so plan ahead before going to horse shows and races. The program should only be administered by a veterinarian because of the possibility of a horse's becoming sensitized due to an allergic reaction. Most horses have a degree of swelling at the injection site and show stiffness in joints for three or four days. Antibiotics are usually given, but refrain from using antibiotics if the temperature is less than 102.5 degrees Fahrenheit, as the disease may be suppressed and spread throughout the body. Relapse will usually occur if the lymph nodes do not abscess and rupture.

In any place where horses congregate, don't use the common watering trough or manger. Use your own buckets with water fresh from the faucet. Isolate all animals recently received from shows or sales. Disinfect all equipment or vehicles where sick horses have been and burn contaminated bedding.

Two types of *equine influenza*, viruses A^1 and A^2, have been identified. Usually, the disease is not serious if promptly treated with antibiotics. Young horses are susceptible to both, while older horses are more likely to be susceptible only to A^2. Also, you can control influenza by means of a vaccine given in two doses at two-week intervals. It must be given annually.

In a case of influenza, the horse goes off feed, has a fever up to 105 degrees, a cough, and a nasal discharge. Death is uncommon unless complications such as pneumonia occur. Rest is important, hence adequate recovery time should be given before training or riding start.

More dangerous is a related but different virus with the jaw-breaking name of *equine viral rhinopneumonitis* (EVR). It causes abortion in mares, and sometimes the infected mare does not display the usual flu-like symptoms. EVR is associated with young horses. Sick horses have cold symptoms, runny noses, and high fevers. It is good management, therefore, to separate all young horses from broodmares. A vaccine is available, but immunity is not permanent. Once begun, the vaccination program must be continued with all horses on the farm, since it has introduced the EVR virus to the farm.

Another virus respiratory disease that can cause abortion, *viral arteritis*, reveals itself by redness in and around the eyes and with swollen eyelids. Other swellings appear on the legs, abdomen, sheath, and mammary glands. The horse seems weak, depressed, loses weight and suffers from colic and diarrhea as well as fever.

Although seriously ill, most horses recover from arteritis. They may remain carriers of the disease, and should be isolated from other horses for upwards of one month. Do not use an affected stallion for breeding until a month or more after his complete recovery.

The *heaves* or "broken wind" (technically, chronic pulmonary emphysema) doesn't happen to horses on pasture. It appears to be a disease of the stable, so that owners of stabled horses must be especially careful. The exact cause remains undetermined, although dusty, moldy hay is blamed; it is thought to be an allergic condition in which the lungs are enlarged and the alveoli rupture.

The sick horse literally heaves; he also has trouble breathing. He takes a deep breath, then as he exhales he gives the diaphragm an extra push. He develops a barrel chest, with a "heave line" marking the labored expiration. When exercised, he is short of wind and has a chronic cough.

Treatment is not very successful; in any case, the wind-broken animal will never again be completely serviceable. Again, the best preventive is good management. Ventilate your stable, prevent dustiness, and be particular about the quality of roughage. Beet pulp in the ration as a roughage has aided in elimination of signs of the heaves.

OTHER SERIOUS DISEASES

Colitis X. It is an acute, usually fatal, non-contagious disease. The exact cause is unknown. It has been noted as a secondary shock syndrome. It occurs after a horse has a second shock or stress such as shipping or return to training before recovering from a disease, usually a respiratory one.

The affected horse is severely depressed, with a high temperature, fast and shallow breathing, possibly signs of colic, followed by severe diarrhea. He can die within three to twenty-four hours. Treatment is non-specific and usually not successful. If your sick horse does pull through, give him plenty of time to recover.

Tetanus. Lockjaw should never occur in horses since it is readily prevented today by immunizing shots. An annual booster is required after initial immunization, with two injections at six-week intervals. Puncture wounds and lacerations are usually produced by nails and splinters and provide an ideal environment for the tetanus organism. Signs of the disease are stiffness in the jaws and hind limbs; then the animal assumes a sawhorse stance with the tail stiffly extended. An immediate dose of the tetanus antitoxin may still save him. Persons who work around horses should also take the tetanus shots for their own protection.

Sleeping sickness (equine encephalomyelitis) causes concern to some people because human beings can catch a similar disease of the central nervous system. However, man cannot catch it from a horse. The carriers are wild birds. The bites of a mosquito or other blood-sucking insects transmit the virus from a bird to other animals.

The sick horse may act in a bizarre manner, walking into walls. Once down, he may be unable to rise; his front legs move as if in running. Even if he survives, the horse is often a useless "dummy" because of damage to brain or spinal cord.

Consider the unfortunate horse as a sentinel warning his master of the presence of sleeping sickness in the area. Annual immunization with two doses of bivalent vaccine administered seven days apart is recommended. The bivalent vaccine protects against both the Eastern and Western types. Also, don't forget to control mosquitoes.

Piroplasmosis. It is caused by a blood parasite which is transmitted by ticks. It was unknown among horses in the United States until 1961, when first diagnosed in Florida. The afflicted horse's gait is unsteady; he lowers his head and spreads out his feet slightly. A distinctive yellow paleness (yellow jaundice) appears in the mucous membranes of the mouth and eyes. Temperature rises to about 105.3 degrees and the disease lasts for eight to ten days. Most horses recover fully in about a month but continue as carriers—likely sources of infection for other animals. To prevent piroplasmosis, control ticks with the same sprays or dips used on cattle, and sprinkle tick powder in the horse's ears. There is no vaccine available.

Swamp fever (equine infectious anemia). This is a very dangerous virus disease because no certain means of treatment or vaccination exists. Just how the virus spreads is not known for sure, but it attacks the red blood cells and leaves the animal weak, depressed, with fever attacks reaching 108 degrees. He hangs his head low; shifts his hind feet forward under his body; and his legs and lower chest wall may swell.

Some horses appear to carry the virus in their blood, but show no symptoms; they serve as a source of virulent blood transmitted to other horses by insects such as mosquitoes or contaminated hypodermic needles. Upon positive diagnosis, the infected animal must be destroyed and the carcass burned or buried. Wherever this disease is identified, employ drastic sanitation measures to isolate suspected animals and disinfect all equipment. Instruments contaminated by this virus must be boiled for a minimum of fifteen minutes to insure that it is killed.

"Tying up" syndrome. This involves the muscles of the hindquarters and back. In the days of draft horses, *azoturia* or "Monday morning disease," was rather common. The horse would seem reluctant to move, like his sluggish master. It's seldom seen today, but a mild or a modified form is observed among race horses and pleasure horses under heavy training or exercise. A "tying up" or hardening of muscle of the croup or loins is accompanied by pain and a stiffened gait. The

urine turns a brownish color. It is theorized that there is a decreased blood flow at the time of increased need, because of spasms of the small arteries which supply the affected muscles.

Usually, the effects wear off in a short time, but watch for it after rigorous exercise, especially if the horse is out of condition: for example, a young horse that is too fat, or one that has not been exercised for several days, but fed a full ration. Vitamin E and selenium treatment have given good results.

Rabies (*hydrophobia*). It is a virus that infects horses and man. The bite of a "mad" dog, a skunk, a fox, and certain bats are all dangerous. The rabid horse seems to go mad, charging other animals and solid objects, or biting himself in the area where the rabid animal bit him.

There is no treatment and almost no hope of recovery. Stray dogs should be discouraged around horses, not only because of rabies but because they often panic a horse into running through fences, or otherwise injuring himself.

DISEASES OF THE FOAL

The newborn foal generally is vigorous and hardy. The mare's first milk gives him antibodies to ward off many infections. Nevertheless, the breeder should be on the lookout during the critical first ten days of life. Fever, bad breath, a coated tongue, and yellowness around the eye are danger signs. Temperature of a foal at rest varies from 100.2 to 101.2 degrees.

Strep infections (*streptococcic*) reveal themselves by diarrhea and in swollen, tender, feverish joints. A swollen hock may seem to recover, but then an ankle gets sore, then the hock again. The foal usually refuses to nurse or to move around much. Antibiotics and other drugs can save him, if the disease is caught early.

"Sleeper" or "dummy" foals are victims of an infectious microorganism called *Shigella equuli*. The sleeper, too weak to rise, lies in a semi-coma. The dummy can stand and walk, but he will bump into walls, often causing himself pain, until exhausted. Neither will he suckle or nurse a bottle. Untended, they may die within a week. But quick action with streptomycin can save them. Today, a large percentage of cases recover and survive as useful animals.

So-called jaundiced (*neonatal isoerythrolysis*) foals do not have an infection, but a congenital blood disorder akin to the Rh factor problem in human babies. The red blood cell types of the foal and dam were incompatible. The foal seems active and lively at birth, but in a day or so it rapidly weakens. The mare's colostrum makes the foal ill, because it contains hostile antibodies. Its eyes and mouth turn pale and yellow, and the foal soon dies.

Prompt blood transfusions may save him, but the best preventive is to give the sire and dam a blood test *before* breeding. If the incompatibility is discovered after breeding, muzzle the foal for forty-eight hours to prevent him from receiving the colostrum. While he is being fed by bottle or by a nurse mare, the dam is milked out hourly until her milk becomes free of antibodies. Then the foal can return to normal nursing, and will probably be all right. See Chapter 16 for bottle-feeding formulas.

With all foals: (1) provide sanitary foaling facilities; (2) disinfect navel cord; (3) make regular and careful observations; and (4) call your veterinarian at the first sign of trouble.

Chapter 14

Parasites, Pests, and Preventives

INTERNAL PARASITES

Internal parasites are one of the most serious problems of the horse industry, not because they cannot be controlled and prevented but because many horse owners are totally unaware of the seriousness of the problem.

A parasite is an animal or plant that lives in, on, or with another living organism, called its host, at the latter's expense. The host of the parasite provides food and shelter. Approximately 150 kinds of parasites affect horses, and it is a rare horse indeed that does not harbor some. Luckily, some parasites are merely annoying guests. But others are so serious a threat as to cause sickness and death.

Recent figures released by the U.S. Department of Agriculture showed an average annual loss to the horse industry in excess of $1,000,000 from bloodworms, large roundworms, piroplasmosis and bots. Some $158,000 worth of horses actually died; however, the greatest loss was from lowered efficiency of performance, reproduction, feed utilization, and from the cost of treatment.

Your horse may have a heavy parasite infection and yet seem normal.

Signs of internal parasites may include unthriftiness, rough hair coat, emaciation, weakness, tucked-up flanks, distended abdomen, tail rubbing, intermittent lameness, chronic cough, anemia, and colic. A veterinarian treating a horse for parasites puts a specimen of manure under his microscope to identify the kind and number of parasites and thus the proper drug to use for "worming."

Strongyles are classified as either large or small. The small ones do little damage. The larger but still relatively small strongyles are commonly called "bloodworms" and include the most dangerous parasite, *Strongylus vulgaris*. The female lays thousands of eggs which are deposited on the ground in the manure. After these eggs hatch the larvae crawl up a blade of grass, which is eaten by the horse, thus starting the life cycle anew. Nearly invisible, the larvae burrow into the wall of small arteries, where they do severe damage during their migration. They cause inflammation and blood clots in the large arteries supplying the intestines. Such blockages of blood flow may result in frequent colic. Furthermore, the wall of the artery may be weakened to such an extent that it ruptures and death occurs.

Interference with digestion, stunting of growth, and poor performance are the most common results of parasitism. Circulatory interference may lead to lameness.

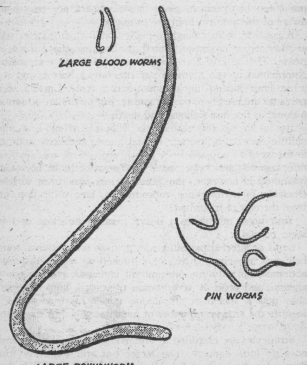

LARGE BLOOD WORMS

PIN WORMS

LARGE ROUNDWORM

Ascarids are long, white "roundworms" sometimes found in the manure. The adult reaches a size of nine to twelve inches. Eggs deposited in the intestine by adult females pass out in the manure. If swallowed by the horse, the infective larva is liberated in the small intestine, where it penetrates the intestinal wall, migrating to the liver, heart, and lungs. After about a week in the lungs the larvae are coughed up and reswallowed. Young ascarids may be present in the intestine when the horse is only four weeks of age, but eggs are not seen in the manure until the horse is eleven to twelve weeks of age. As the animal gets older he develops an immunity to these parasites; however, ascarids are normally not found in horses beyond three or four years of age.

"Cold," cough, and even pneumonia may be caused by the larvae. Because of their size and number, these worms consume large amounts of nutrients, so that the young horse does not grow and develop as rapidly as it should. Heavy infection may cause a mechanical blockage of the intestine.

The pinworm (*Oxyuris equi*) grows to a length of two or three inches in the lower digestive tract. It may sometimes be seen crawling halfway out of the anus to lay its eggs; at other times the eggs are passed in the manure. Grayish-white encrusted material around the anus is generally a sign of pinworms. Though not otherwise damaging, they cause irritation under the tail. The horse will rub his tail and rearquarters against an object, thus often rubbing the hair out of the tail.

Bots are not true worms but the larvae of the botfly (*Gastrophilus*). You may notice these flies, resembling small bees,

BOT FLY

BOT LARVA

buzzing around a horse's forelegs. Other varieties of botfly favor the throat or the lips and nose. They do not sting, but lay eggs visible as little yellow capsules sticking to the hairs of the foreleg. The horse gets them into his stomach by biting or licking that area. The bot larvae attach to the lining of the stomach. They steal nourishment from the horse and may, in extremely severe cases, damage the stomach to such an extent that it ruptures.

PREVENTION AND TREATMENT

Drugs known as anthelmintics are used in combating parasites. Some of the various anthelmintics include piperazine, phenothiazine, carbon disulfide and combinations thereof, and the newer ones, trichlorfon and thiabendazole.

Strongyles, large and small, can be treated by phenothiazine, a piperazine-phenothiazine combination, and thiabendazole. Thiabendazole is an especially effective drug against large strongyles.

Ascarids are prevalent only in young horses. Piperazine, a piperazine-phenothiazine combination, trichlorfon and thiabendazole are highly effective in the treatment of ascarids.

Pinworms are generally controlled by the drugs that are used against ascarids and strongyles. Piperazine, a piperazine-phenothiazine combination, and thiabendazole have been used effectively.

If bots are known to be a problem in your area, treat your horse for them at least once a year—in the late fall to early winter, after the second or third killing frost. Carbon disulfide has been the traditional treatment, and should be given by your veterinarian. Organic phosphates such as trichlorfon are also effective.

Administration of anthelmintics may be by stomach tube, bolus (large pill), dose syringe or sprinkled on the feed. Naturally, the latter method is an advantage to horse owners; however, the drug must be palatable and have a relatively wide safety margin in case a horse is overdosed. Some drugs have a narrow safety range. They are poison to the parasites, but in excess they may also be poison to the horse. Thiabendazole possesses a wide safety margin. Care should be exercised in the handling of all drugs; always follow the directions on the label, or those given by your veterinarian.

Horses may show strongyle egg counts as high as 3,000

per gram with no noticeable signs of infection, provided they are on a high plane of nutrition. Egg numbers in the manure reach a peak in late summer, just in time to infest the pasture that will be grazed by the foal. A mare should be treated against strongyles one month before foaling, and again ten days afterward.

Foals are born free of worms but soon pick them up from the pasture. Treat with piperazine or thiabendazole for ascarids at eight weeks of age, and again every two months for a year. Large strongyles appear at the twentieth to twenty-fifth week of life; thiabendazole is very effective against them. A combination of phenothiazine and piperazine is also effective.

A program of prevention will do much to keep the parasite problem within manageable limits. Here is a checklist to follow:

1. Dispose of manure (see Chapter 7).
2. Do not feed hay or grain on the ground or floor, where it may be contaminated with parasite eggs and larvae. Do not use hay for bedding, since the horse may eat it.
3. Do not allow horses to drink water from stagnant ponds which could have been contaminated by drainage.
4. If the stall floor is of clay or earth, dig it up about five to six inches each year and replace with clean clay or earth.
5. Do not overstock your pastures. Use a rotational grazing program to break up the life cycle of the parasites.
6. Clip pastures regularly; this exposes the larvae to the killing environmental forces and at the same time promotes new, lush growth of the pasture.
7. Give young horses a parasite-free pasture, if possible, since they are more susceptible to parasite infection than are older horses.
8. Let cattle or sheep graze a pasture formerly grazed by horses. They are not affected by the same parasites; thus the horse parasites will die.
9. In cases of severe pasture infestation, keep horses entirely off the pasture for several months. (In order to do this one must have other pastures.) Chain harrowing has been recommended to expose the eggs and larvae to the environment, but it has the decided dis-

advantage of scattering the eggs and larvae over a wide area.

10. Control flies.

11. To prevent bot reinfection, remove the bot eggs from the horse. When you see the eggs on the horse's foreleg—or other parts of the body—wash with warm water and rub briskly with a sponge; this hatches the eggs and the larvae soon die. Apply equal parts of mineral oil and kerosene to kill any that are left. Clipping the legs is also helpful.

EXTERNAL PARASITES

External parasites are not as serious a problem as internal ones, but they are also often neglected.

Lice may be either the biting or sucking type. Suspect them when the horse rubs against objects, and has rough hair on the withers, head, or near the tail. Horses that are poorly groomed and stabled, especially during the winter and early spring, are most likely to become infested. Proper grooming and feeding, as well as clean stables and equipment, help prevent lice. Infested horses may be sprayed, sponged, or dusted with a product containing Ciodrin, pyrethrins, rotenone, malathion, methoxychlor, DDT, lindane or ronnel. Two treatments a couple of weeks apart usually are necessary to destroy any eggs that hatch after the first treatment.

Mange is caused by tiny mites that burrow into the skin. It is difficult to eradicate. Mange causes irritation, itching, and inflammation. Use lindane or rotenone with wettable sulphur, spraying or wetting with a brush, whichever works better; repeat the treatment every seven days.

Ticks are dangerous to man as well as to the horse since they may carry the organisms of Rocky Mountain spotted fever. (They also carry the parasite that causes piroplasmosis.) In the horse they are usually found in the flank area, in or around the ears, and in the mane and tail. Effective pesticides include DDT, toxaphene, lindane, malathion, and ronnel.

Horses and ponies get *ringworm* (a fungus disease) usually on the head, neck, or at the base of the tail. A hairless, rounded lesion appears, about the size of a quarter dollar. The horse may exhibit signs of itching. If only a few lesions occur, use warm water and soap to soften and remove the crust, dry and apply iodine daily for a week or two. If lesions are more extensive, consult with your veterinarian. Use rubber gloves to avoid infecting yourself with ringworm.

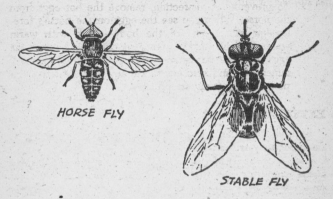

HORSE FLY

STABLE FLY

Insects such as *flies* and *mosquitoes* are a great annoyance to the horse, even though Nature provides him with a fly-swatter—his tail. Some horses are bothered so much by flies that they may lose considerable weight during fly season. Insects are disease carriers, too.

Houseflies and face flies do not bite, but feed on secretions from the animal's skin, eyes, and nose. Horn flies, stable flies, mosquitoes, deer flies and horseflies bite and suck blood. (See also botflies, above.) Use screens and good sanitation methods to eliminate breeding places; especially, drain any low swampy areas.

Turning horses out at night rather than during the day is helpful in the fly season. A pole barn with just a roof shades the sun and allows the breeze to blow through, keeping insects away.

Carefully read and follow directions when applying insecticides. Various methods that may be helpful in controlling flies are spraying of buildings, use of fly baits and treated strands or cords; horses may be sprayed or sponged regularly. Products containing pyrethrins, Ciodrin, DDVP, malathion, or ronnel are useful. Caution: do not contaminate feed, water, or feed and water equipment.

Summer sores result when house or stable flies deposit *Habronema* larvae in skin wounds. These sores will disappear after frost, apparently healed, but may reoccur the following summer. The only control method is effective control of flies. Adult *Habronema* that live in the intestinal tract are known as stomach worms.

Chapter 15

Breeding for Pleasure and Profit

One of the thrills as a horse owner is raising a foal. More and more people have discovered the challenge and joy of aiding nature to create a new young animal. In the breed associations, many thousands of members raise only one or two foals a year. Some may be bred for profit, but all give pleasure.

Care is of the utmost importance for success in breeding horses. In domestication, horses are far less prolific than in the wild state. On our Western plains, a mature stallion led a band of 30 to 40 mares. In the spring when the grass came up green and lush, the mares foaled and soon afterward were rebred by the stallion. A foaling rate of 90 percent was common, meaning that 90 out of 100 mares would bear a live foal. Compare this with a rate of only 50 to 60 percent in domestic horses.

In nature the horses selected the best environment. They moved freely over a vast grazing area, following the grass into the mountains each spring and summer, and wintered in the valleys. Undoubtedly, in nature the contamination and infection of mares which plague horse breeding today was considerably less.

The wild stallion would mate several times with each mare during her heat period, thus improving the chances of mating at the most fertile moment. The natural breeding season was longer, too. Foals were born in late spring and summer, often as late as August. Today, for economic reasons, horse breeding is cut short about July 1. Few foals are born later than the beginning of June.

The pressure for early foals stems from the common birth date of January 1 for all registered horses. A year or two later, a March foal will be bigger on the average than a June foal, a distinct advantage for purposes of racing, showing, or sale.

Still another reason for low fertility is simply lack of understanding on the part of many horseowners. Often the advent of heat in the mare goes unnoticed, or the wrong time is chosen for mating the mare to the stallion. On a stud farm, one mature stallion may be mated to between 50 and 100 mares by natural service. Yet only 25 to 60 of these mares will produce a live foal the next spring.

Artificial insemination (A.I.) has been used to increase the number of mares mated to a stallion in one season. As many as several hundred mares may thus be impregnated from a single stallion in one season. However, some breed associations will not register A.I. offspring. Others will permit the use of A.I. providing that insemination occurs on the premises where the stallion stands and that the semen is neither shipped nor frozen.

WHEN TO BREED A FILLY

More people are apt to own a mare than a stallion; therefore, more emphasis will be placed upon the mare. What is the earliest age at which a filly may be bred? Puberty, the beginning of sexual maturity, normally occurs at twelve to eighteen months of age. Liberal feeding will result in early sexual maturity; a low plane of nutrition will retard it. In practice, most fillies are bred for the first time at three years old, bearing a foal at four years. This gives the filly a year or more for racing or showing as a two-year-old.

Generally, it is not a recommended practice to breed two-year-old fillies to foal as three-year-olds except under conditions of excellent management. Size, rather than age, is a more practical guide to the proper time for first breeding, since size is a good indicator of sexual maturity. The feeding program must supply the need of maintenance, growth, and pregnancy. In the subsequent year, there is the added requirement of lactation. So, only with a high plane of nutrition and excellent management should two-year-old fillies be bred. Also, it is often difficult to get them in foal.

The mare's normal reproductive life lasts to about nineteen years of age. Therefore, a mare first foaling at four years of age has an expected productive span of fifteen years. At the average rate of 50 percent, she would produce six to seven foals—not very efficient compared to other farm animals. The modern animal science and veterinary medicine can extend the reproductive life of a mare. Some mares as old as twenty-six have been known to produce normal, healthy foals.

Several problems exist in breeding old mares. They may be difficult to get in foal, especially if they miss one or two years of producing. General health may become a factor. Also, contamination of the vulva may result in a uterine infection.

REPRODUCTIVE TRACT OF THE MARE

A discussion of the reproductive tract of the mare will give horse owners a better knowledge of reproduction in the mare. See the illustration below. The external opening, the vulva, prevents foreign material from entering the reproductive tract. The "windsucker" is an example of what happens when the vulva does not function properly.

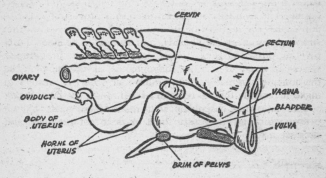

DIAGRAM OF MARE'S REPRODUCTIVE TRACT

The vagina, the outermost part of the reproductive tract, serves as a receptacle of semen and as a passageway for the delivery of the foal. A thick annular muscle which separates vagina and uterus, the cervix, also prevents entry of foreign material into the uterus. The cervix is open during estrus (heat) and at parturition, while during pregnancy a thick, mucus material called "cervical plug" seals off the canal.

The fetus develops in the uterus, which consists of two horns and a body. At the end of each horn a small tube, the Fallopian tube or oviduct, forms a pathway for the egg (ovum) from the ovary to the uterus. It is in the oviduct that fertilization and early development normally occur. The end of the oviduct spreads out in a funnel shape and is called the infundibulum.

The kidney-shaped ovaries are located near the kidney and are the source of the eggs and certain hormones. The egg develops in a follicle, a fluid-filled sac.

The function of the reproductive tract and the mare's mating behavior are regulated by a delicately balanced system of hormones produced by the pituitary gland and the ovaries. The pituitary, a small gland at the base of the brain, releases into the bloodstream several hormones in which we are interested: FSH, LH, and prolactin. FSH (follicle stimulating hormone) stimulates the ovaries to produce a follicle and estrogen. LH (luteinizing hormone) causes ovulation of the egg and the subsequent development of the corpus luteum (yellow body) in the site of the ruptured follicle. Prolactin stimulates milk secretion and the production of progesterone. The ovaries produce estrogen and progestrone. Estrogen causes the mare to come into heat and at the same time, suppresses the release of FSH, and stimulates release of LH by the pituitary. The yellow body produces progestrone which is essential for the maintenance of pregnancy. The ovaries also produce relaxin, which reacts on the muscles to make it possible for the fetus to pass through the birth canal.

The following discussion will relate these facts to the events which are necessary for a mare to get pregnant and produce a foal.

ESTRUS

Heat is the period of sexual receptivity when the mare will accept the stallion. Mares average five to seven days in heat. Sexual activity normally lasts from February to October each year. The mare is a "long day breeder," that is, as the days lengthen in spring and summer, she comes in heat. In contrast, sheep are "short day breeders," they mate as daylight diminishes in the fall. This phenomenon is related to the effect of sunlight on the pituitary gland. The lush pastures of spring are a good source of protein, vitamins, and minerals. Many horsemen insist that there is no point in breeding mares until green grass comes and they shed their winter coats.

Each mare exhibits a rather definite pattern. If a mare is in heat for six days, she will be rather consistent through successive cycles. A good horseman keeps records of each mare's heat periods. The length of heat period is generally longer in old mares, underfed mares, and during the early part of the breeding season.

ESTROUS CYCLE

The number of days from the start of one estrus to the start of the next is called the estrous cycle. It ranges from eighteen to thirty-seven days and averages about twenty-one days.

The longer the heat period, the longer the cycle. Thus a mare in estrus four or five days will have an estrous cycle of eighteen or nineteen days, whereas a mare in heat for seven or eight days will have a twenty-one or a twenty-two day cycle. The cycle tends to be longer in young, old, and thin or underfed mares, because of a slower ripening of the ova.

Estrus does not occur while a mare is pregnant. All mares should be checked each fall for breeding condition. This allows time to correct any problems. Better nutrition improves the regularity of the estrous cycle and the chances for conception. (See Chapter 12 on feeding.)

OVULATION

For the horse breeder, the significant moment in the mare's reproductive process is ovulation—the release of an egg from a follicle on an ovary. Generally, this occurs twenty-four to forty-eight hours before the mare goes out of heat.

The luteinizing hormone which causes ovulation is so low in some mares that they do not ovulate. This is a more serious problem in mares than in other animals. By rectal palpation after heat, a veterinarian can determine if a mare has ovulated or not. Mating must be synchronized with time of ovulation for optimum chance of fertilization. All breeding plans hinge upon this natural time clock.

TIMING THE ESTRUS

Mating should occur ideally from six to twelve hours before ovulation. The time of ovulation can be determined by various tests and by experience with a given mare in previous estrus periods.

Signs of heat are frequent urination, slightly raised tail, a relaxed or "winking" vulva, and a vaginal discharge noticeable on the quarter, hocks, and tail. The mare normally will not "show" heat by her actions to other mares or to geldings, but she will to a stallion. He is brought nearby to tease (check) the mare.

Teasing indicates when the estrus begins and when it ends, but it is not 100 percent reliable. Some mares do not "show" to the teaser and have a quiet estrus, while other mares will show signs of heat and yet be in foal. By regular teasing the length of heat can be established and one can estimate the approximate time of ovulation. The veterinarian has two other techniques, a speculum examination of the vagina and cervix, and rectal palpation of the ovaries. Rectal palpation is commonly practiced on well-managed stud farms to determine the size of the follicle and to approximate the time of ovulation, since the follicle becomes soft and flabby about twenty-four hours before ovulation. This gives the mares being serviced the best chance for fertilization.

FERTILIZATION

Ovulation timing is the key to success because the sperm cells live only a short while, from twenty-four to seventy-two hours after being deposited in the mare. The egg cell also has a short life, about twelve hours after ovulation. It takes the sperm from six to twelve hours to travel up to the Fallopian tube, the site of fertilization—the union of sperm and egg. If fertilization occurs when the egg or sperm is either senile or immature, the embryo may die. The fertilization rate of mares is 80 to 85 percent, although only 50 to 60 percent produce foals. This indicates a high rate of embryonic death which might have been prevented by mating at the proper time.

A rule of thumb: keep good teasing records during the estrous cycle to determine the mare's length of estrus and to deduce the approximate ovulation time, or have the veterinarian determine the time precisely by rectal palpation. Mate the mare to the stallion no more than twelve hours before ovulation. Normally when records are unavailable mares are mated on the fourth day and every other day until they go out of heat.

GESTATION

When a sperm has fertilized the egg, the union of the two sex cells, or gametes, is known as a zygote. It takes the zygote from two to five days to travel down the Fallopian tube into the uterus. By this time it has grown into an embryo, somewhat resembling a mulberry. During the next nine to thirteen weeks it remains free-floating, not attached to the uterine wall. Uterine milk, fluids of the uterus, nourish the embryo.

This is a dangerous period. A kick or some other injury may result in the loss of the unattached embryo. If the mare returns to heat sixty to ninety days after being bred ("repeat breeding"), an abortion may be suspected.

Gestation, the period of pregnancy from conception to birth, normally takes 340 days plus or minus a twenty-day deviation. A rule of thumb: to forecast the foaling date, subtract one month from the day the mare was bred and add four days. For example, a mare bred on May 5 should foal April 9 of the following year.

These eleven months are a trying time for mare owners, who can only wait anxiously for the results of their planning. A failure can be a great economic loss. Because of the low conception rate of horses, owners of both mare and stallion want to detect pregnancy as early as possible.

Teasing is the frequent method; if not pregnant, the mare should show to the teaser again in fourteen or fifteen days. This test is not positive enough; there are more definite methods. A blood test similar to the "rabbit test" in humans can be performed from the forty-fifth to the one hundredth day of pregnancy. A chemical test for estrogen in the urine is accurate from the one hundred-twentieth day until birth. But the quickest, most accurate test is rectal palpation at forty to fifty days after mating.

Even if a mare is found to be pregnant in spring or early summer, it is a good practice to check again in the fall. Many things can cause an abortion. If the mare is not in foal, the veterinarian has time before the next breeding season to find the cause of barrenness and correct it. This is economical in the long run, especially with a valuable mare.

A FOAL IS BORN

Parturition or birth is a critical moment for both mare and man. It is just as exciting and adventuresome for the ardent horse breeder as it is for the novice. Be prepared beforehand to give the mare and foal proper care. As the time approaches, look for these physical signs. From two to six weeks before foaling, the mare's udder fills and becomes distended. Then about seven to ten days prior to foaling, the muscles around the tail relax, giving the area a concave or sunken appearance. Also the stomach seems to drop. The teats fill out about four to six days before birth, and milk may drop from them in large quantity. Wax may appear on the ends of the teats two to four days ahead, but this doesn't always happen.

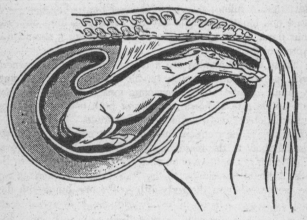

Normal Position of Foal at Birth

The signs immediately before foaling are a restlessness in the mare, frequent urination, and breaking out into a sweat. Occasionally she will turn her head to the rear and nicker as if calling the foal. Sometimes all signs fail and a foal is born when least expected. This, of course, is part of the excitement.

In nature the mare foals out in the open. She goes off by herself and will find a safe place. Normally she does a very good job alone, in the natural way. The main reason for providing a shelter is to give assistance in case it is needed.

Early in the year, shelter should be provided as protection from the weather, particularly in cold areas. Foaling may occur in a barn or in a small pasture with an open shed. The ideal is a stall about 14 x 14 feet, well lighted and ventilated, clean, disinfected, well bedded, and clear of any low manger or hay rack which could cause injury.

About two hours before foaling, wrap the mare's tail in a bandage to keep it clean and out of the way. The external genitals, buttocks, and udder should be washed with warm soapy water or a mild disinfectant.

Any person watching the mare should stay as quiet and as inconspicuous as possible. It's a good idea to place the foaling stall next to an office with a protected window, so the mare can be observed without becoming nervous. And don't you get nervous watching the mare! There is a temptation to rush things and offer too much assistance. Let nature take her course; she has been at it a lot longer. The foal will arrive in due time.

Hard labor starts with the rupture of the water bag and discharge of what is called amniotic fluids. Normally, once a mare is in labor she will foal within fifteen minutes, but it may take more than two hours, which indicates complications. If any complications occur or if inexperienced, a veterinarian should be called. Prior arrangements with him are a wise precaution.

The foal is delivered front feet first with the heels down, the head resting on the front legs. The shoulders, body, hips, hindlegs, and hindfeet follow. Several abnormal positions occur, but generally are not much of a problem. Once delivery starts, it's best for the foal to emerge quickly. Should the umbilical cord break before the head is delivered, the foal's oxygen supply from the mother is shut off and he may smother.

CARE OF THE NEWBORN FOAL

Here is one of the true miracles of nature. A newborn foal

is a thrill for young people especially, but no one ever out-grows the excitement in seeing one.

The very first step is to remove any materials from the foal's nostrils and mouth that may restrict breathing. Actually this may be done as the foal is being born. Place a thumb and forefinger on either side of the nose. Using a light pressure, slide them down the muzzle, as if emptying a tube of toothpaste. Next, rub the foal dry with clean straw or a rag —quite important in cold weather. Usually the mare will take care of things herself by getting up and licking the foal dry. Massaging the body also helps to start the foal breathing.

Don't cut the umbilical cord which is the connecting link between the mare and the fetus. Usually it is broken by the thrashing foal. If not, break it off close to the foal's body. Place it between the forefinger and second finger, and press with the thumb on the opposite side. The ragged break will not hemorrhage, whereas a knife cut would. Treat the navel stump with iodine to prevent infection. An injection of pen-icillin-streptomycin is often given to help prevent early infections.

The mare's first milk, the colostrum, is nature's own way of providing a concentrated source of milk which is easily digested. The colostrum is high in protein and vitamin A. It contains antibodies to fight infections until the young foal can produce these materials himself. Make sure he receives the colostrum. Some large farms have colostrum banks, like blood banks, to collect and store the invaluable first milk from mares that bear dead foals.

Sometimes a weak foal needs help in nursing. Maiden mares may get excited and not let the foal suckle, or don't know what it is all about and may need some aid. Usually, just let the foal thrash around by himself; this strengthens the muscles.

The foal should defecate within four to twelve hours after birth. Often he is seen to strain; elevation and vigorous swishing of the tail are signs of constipation. It is caused by an accumulation of hard balls of feces, called meconium, in the large intestine during the gestation period. The colostrum milk, being slightly laxative, will usually take care of it. If not, give the foal an enema consisting of 2 quarts of warm soapy water. Let the water flow in gently by gravity; do not force it. Watch the foal carefully during the first twelve hours. If he does not defecate by that time or continues to strain frequently, the problem can be serious. (See Chapter 14 for symptoms of disease.)

FEEDING THE MARE

Just before foaling time, reduce the grain allowance of the mare by about one-fourth. Use wheat bran in the diet, since it is bulky and laxative. The foaling mare should be in good thrifty condition, neither fat nor poor. After foaling, when she is exhausted and sweating, give her a small amount of lukewarm water.

Her first couple of feedings should be a hot bran mash, equal to about half her normal amount of feed. This helps to regulate the bowels with less straining and pressure on the reproductive tract. Then begin increasing the grain allowance to bring the mare up to maximum level at about twenty days, as needed for lactation. (See Chapter 12 on feeding.)

At about nine days, the young foal is subject to scouring or diarrhea. This is during the mare's foal heat and excess estrogen in the milk may be the cause. Also, too much milk or poor digestion of milk may be factors. By your under-feeding the mare to keep the milk flow below maximum level at this time, the foal will have less tendency to scour.

BOTTLE FEEDING

Sometimes, unhappily, a foaling mare dies of accident or disease. In the absence of a nurse mare, you will have to bottle-feed the foal. Cow's milk is higher in fat and lower in sugar (lactose) than mare's milk. Adjust it to the young horse's needs by either of these formulas:

(1)

4 ounces skimmed cow's milk
1 teaspoon corn syrup

(2)

1 8-ounce can evaporated milk

(3)

8 ounces cow's milk
8 ounces lime water
1 teaspoon sugar

1 8-ounce can water
4 tablespoons lime water
1 tablespoon corn syrup

Feeding Schedule

First 2 days: 4 to 8 ounces of formula every hour
Next 5 days: Same every 2 hours
Next 3 weeks: Same every 4 hours
At one month: Four feedings daily

By this time the foal may eat some grain. A good creep feed ration:

80 percent rolled oats   10 percent soybean meal
10 percent wheat bran   Brown sugar, added as appetizer
          Alfalfa hay (if good pasture is not available)

Raising an orphan foal takes time, patience, loss of sleep, and a lot of hard work. But it is fantastically rewarding to watch the baby animal survive. Follow these guidelines with all newborn foals:

1. Provide sanitary foaling facilities.
2. Disinfect navel cord.
3. Give tetanus antitoxin and antibiotics.
4. Administer an enema if there is no bowel movement within the first 12 hours.
5. Make regular, careful observations.
6. Call your veterinarian at the *first* sign of trouble.

WHEN TO REBREED

A big question among horsemen is when to rebreed after foaling. The mare comes into heat (foal heat) again in about seven to nine days. It is nature's way of cleaning the mare. To mate her again at this time is not recommended—although many horsemen do it in order to get an earlier foal the following year. There are several facts that should be considered in making this decision. Any mare that had difficulty at foaling, or had a retained placenta (afterbirth) for longer than an hour, a placenta weighing more than 14 pounds, a dead or diseased foal, or any abnormal discharge after foaling should not be rebred at the foal heat. If none of these conditions exists, a vaginal examination by a veterinarian is necessary before mating to be sure the vagina is free from un-healed lacerations or bruises which may have occurred during foaling. A cervical smear at this time will indicate if the mare is free from infection. Only under these conditions is it good management to breed on the foal heat. Otherwise it is best to rebreed at the first normal heat period, following foal heat, about 27 days after the birth.

MANAGEMENT OF THE STALLION

The stallion reaches puberty later than the filly, at about eighteen to twenty-four months of age. In the racing breeds, most stallions are four to five years old before being placed in stud. But with other breeds, there is a tendency to use the stallion earlier. Good management then becomes especially important, not only in getting the mares settled (in foal), but in establishing the young stallion's future breeding habits. Most of the bad habits, such as kicking and biting mares, can be traced to poor handling in the early years at stud.

As indicated by the following tables, the older a stallion, the more mares he can service in a season. A two-year-old stallion can be mated only to a limited number of mares, and only if service is spaced out. A stallion being hand mated can service more mares than the same stallion at pasture mating. But a stallion with semen of poor quality cannot get many mares in foal.

NUMBER OF MARES PER STALLION PER SEASON

Age (in years)	Hand mating	Pasture mating
2	10–12	none
3	15–40	20
4	25–60	30
mature	80–100	40
18 & over	20–40	20

NUMBER OF SERVICES PER STALLION

Age (in years)	Hand mating (No. of services per week)
2	2–3 services per week
3	1 per day
4 & over	2 per day*
18 & over	1 per day

* Allow one day of rest per week.

Rectal palpation of the mare's ovaries saves the stallion by eliminating mares not truly ready for mating. Overworking the stallion by mating two or three mares daily often lowers the quality of semen and it is less likely to fertilize the egg. A stallion being mated to a smaller number of mares can be bred daily with one day of rest per week. Or, as often happens, the stallion may be used twice a day for only two or three days during the week.

The owner sells the stallion's services, so the stallion must have the ability to get mares in foal. Early in the season, at about the third or fourth mating, a semen sample should be examined by a qualified veterinarian. Few stallions are actually sterile, but low fertility does occur. If detected early, it may often be corrected. The causes are poor physical condition, infections, injuries, and hereditary factors.

CARE OF STALLIONS

The breeding stallion requires special stabling, such as a box stall in a barn, or a small shed inside a paddock or small pasture. It should be at least 14 by 14 feet of heavy construction. One-inch wood is too light, since a stallion can kick through it; 2 by 6's are desirable.

If housed in a barn, the stallion should have a paddock or exercise area large enough to contain some pasture—usually one to three acres. Good pasture is important for its protein, vitamins and mineral content, particularly in the spring.

Just before the breeding season, the stallion should be fed adequate amounts of energy feed, protein, vitamins, and minerals. A vitamin-mineral supplement is usually fed. (See Chapter 12.) But he also needs exercise. Some stallion owners feed well enough, but without exercise the horse will get too fat. Riding is one of the best exercises, and not for just a few minutes, but regularly, for at least three or four miles a day. The stallion may be given free access to a paddock or turned out daily for several hours.

Good grooming is essential for the health of the stallion. It should include checking and cleaning out the feet as well as brushing and checking for cuts or other injuries daily. (See Chapter 8 for grooming techniques.) On some stud farms the stallions are groomed and fed every six hours, or at least three times a day.

Remember, while a mare may produce one foal a year, a stallion may sire 25 or more foals annually. He is important!

Chapter 16

Improving the Breed

The purpose of horse breeding should be to produce, if possible, a better animal than the parents. To accomplish this one uses genetics, the scientific application of the mechanism of inheritance. This is one of the most fascinating, but least understood, tools of horse production. Here we will confine our discussion to a few basic facts to help anyone who wants to breed his mare and raise a foal.

The sperm from the stallion and the egg from the mare are each sex cells—called gametes—of microscopic size. At the moment they unite to create a zygote, the beginning of an embryo, the inheritance of the new foal is determined. The zygote multiplies itself to form new cells. Every cell in the young horse's body will be an exact duplicate of the original zygote in genetic makeup: every cell, that is, except the sex cells.

Each cell contains the carriers of inheritance—chromosomes and genes. Chromosomes are threadlike structures existing in pairs, with genes strung along them like beads on a string. Genes are the units of inheritance; they determine among other things the color, speed, conformation, etc. of your horse. Since chromosomes are in pairs, so are genes. The horse has 32 chromosome pairs, man has 23.

The sex cells—sperm and ova—are unique. As they are formed in the testes of the stallion or in the ovaries of the mare, the chromosome pairs separate. The sex cells have half the number of chromosomes of the body cells; they contain only one member of each pair. The original number is restored when sperm and egg unite. Therefore, the sire and dam each contribute a random sample half of their inheritance to each foal by this process.

Most of the important inherited traits, such as performance ability, are determined by many pairs of genes. This is called quantitative inheritance. Since there are an unknown number of genes on the 32 chromosome pairs, the number of possible combinations becomes astronomical.

BLOODLINES

Horsemen often refer to "percentage of blood" when discussing bloodlines or pedigrees. Only in a direct relationship —where one relative is a direct descendant of the other—can the degree of relationship or "blood" be readily expressed as a percentage. A grandson does have a 25 percent relationship to a grandsire. But the arithmetic breaks down when applied to collateral relatives, those individuals with some of the same ancestors, such as half-brother and cousins.

The objective of breeding horses is to make genetic progress with each generation. The breeder has two tools at hand to accomplish this task: selection and mating systems.

SELECTION

Selection is defined as permitting certain individual animals in a population to produce more offspring than others. The same methods of selection apply in the choice of a horse whether for a 4-H Horse project or for pleasure riding. (See Chapter 15.) These methods are: (1) pedigree selection; (2) mass selection; and (3) progeny test selection.

Great emphasis is placed on pedigree selection—one looks at the performance record of relatives of the individual horse. It is a valuable tool with young animals in which the desired traits have not yet been expressed and for traits which are of low heritability. The emphasis should be placed on *close* relatives; remember that each generation cuts in half the genetic relation of individuals. Just because a great-great-grandsire was a champion show horse or racehorse does not mean much. Too much emphasis is placed on popular pedigrees, too little on sound genetic principles. Rarely should the pedigree receive as much consideration as the animal's own conformation or performance.

Mass selection is based upon the animal's conformation and performance, known as phenotype. If one wants to breed good jumping or pleasure horses, outstanding individuals in these classes should be selected for breeding stock. It is helpful with highly heritable traits. The method may be used when an animal is old enough to exhibit his phenotype. Remember, conformation relates to performance.

Progeny test selection looks at the offspring rather than the individual. A stallion or mare is selected for breeding based upon the conformation and performance of their offspring. Suppose a mare is of good pedigree and phenotype but has not produced foals of proven ability or conformation. She therefore should be rejected. This test is most often applied in the choice of a stallion for one's mare. The individual must be old enough to have produced offspring, so this method of selection can only be used with older animals.

In actual practice, all three methods are combined. In young horses not mature enough for performance, one would look for conformation, pedigree, and the records of collateral relatives (which amount to a progeny test of the horse's sire and dam). In older horses, one would emphasize performance and conformation, also the records (progeny test) of their offspring to date. Usually one selects for several traits at once; this limits the selection pressure which can be placed on any one trait. Greatest emphasis, therefore, should be on the most important economic characteristics.

MATING SYSTEMS

Having selected the breeding stock, one has a choice of four basic systems of mating: inbreeding, linebreeding, outcrossing, and crossbreeding.

Inbreeding is widely misunderstood, because it is generally associated with genetic defects and a reduction of vigor and performance. Possibly for this reason, it has not played as important a role in developing horse breeds as with other livestock. True, inbreeding can bring genetic "trash" to the surface, but scientifically practiced, inbreeding can also produce superior breeding animals.

The word means simply the mating of animals more closely related than the average of the population—having a common ancestor within four to six generations. In practice inbreeding usually refers to parent-offspring or to full-sib (brother-sister) mating. Inbred animals can transmit their characteristics with greater uniformity.

With an inbred stallion, the chances are good that each of

his offspring will receive from him several of the same genes; therefore, they will closely resemble him and one another. Because of the risk, inbreeding should be practiced only with very superior animals and by a breeder with a thorough knowledge of genetics.

Linebreeding aims at maintaining a high degree of relationship to an outstanding individual. Thus the King Ranch has linebred its Quarter Horses to the foundation sire, Old Sorrel. Half-sib or grandsire-to-granddaughter matings are the general rule. To a degree this is inbreeding, but less intense. Again, it should be restricted to superior animals and knowledgeable breeders.

Outcrossing and *crossbreeding* have the opposite effect of inbreeding and linebreeding: they cause dissimilar gene pairs. These animals will not breed as true, but they gain in hybrid vigor, which usually results in greater performance. Conformation tends to improve.

In outcrossing, animals are mated that are of the same breed but having no relationship within four to six generations. It is the most frequently used mating system of the horse industry today. Crossbreeding is the mating of two purebreds or registered animals of different breeds. This was the principle followed in early days that established the modern breeds of horses.

Crossbreeding is recognized only in certain associations. Thus the foal of a Quarter Horse mated to a Thoroughbred may be registered in the American Quarter Horse Association for performance only. After proving its ability and passing inspection for conformation, the animal may be used for breeding.

MATING PLANS

The best known mating plan is to breed the best to the best. Positive breeding is mating a sire with great speed to a mare with great speed or a sire with outstanding show record to a mare with outstanding show record. The opposite is negative breeding. One studies the mare, finds her faults, then mates her to a stallion strong in those characteristics. For example, one might mate a mare that is short and thick in the neck to a stallion that has a clean, lean neck.

ECONOMIC TRAITS

The trait of greatest economic importance in horses is performance. Racing ability has been shown to have a heritability estimate of 60 percent. Two factors determine the difference between animals—heredity and environment. Heritability is the percentage of this difference due to genetics. So, 40 percent of the difference in racing ability comes from environment (nutrition, training, freedom from parasites). A stakes-winning mare bred to a stakes-winning stallion is more likely to produce a stakes winner than two animals of unproven class.

As long as the characteristic is highly heritable, the breeder can make progress by selecting for it. In the Western horse, cow sense is considered inherited. Although there has been no specific proof, certain families through certain sires are noted for their ability to work cattle.

Conformation is of interest to horse owners as each breed is selected for a different type. The heritability of conformation with cattle and sheep is lower than for performance traits. The author feels that this holds true with horses. Environment plays a greater role here. Conformation defects are hereditary, particularly in the skeleton, and most noticeably in the feet and legs. A horse that toes-out tends to pass this defect on to its offspring.

Fertility, another economic value in horses, is hardly inherited at all—perhaps as little as 5 percent. One cannot select for fertility with much hope of success. Improving the horse's environment by nutrition and management offers the best chance of bettering the low, 50 to 60 percent foal crop now produced annually.

Here's wishing that all your horses are champions!

APPENDIX

Objectives of the 4-H Horse Project

1. To develop leadership, initiative, self-reliance, sportsmanship, and other desirable traits of character.
2. To experience the pride of owning a horse or pony and being responsible for its management.
3. To develop an appreciation of horseback riding as a healthy and wholesome form of recreation.
4. To learn skill in horsemanship and an understanding of the business of breeding, raising, and training horses.
5. To increase knowledge of safety precautions to prevent injury to themselves, others, and their mounts.
6. To promote greater love for animals and a humane attitude toward them.
7. To be better prepared for citizenship responsibilities through working in groups and supporting community horse projects and activities.

There were 224,540 members in 1969, compared with 37,531 in 1959. Any boy or girl aged nine to nineteen is eligible. For information, contact the Cooperative Extension Service located in your county.

REFERENCES

Animal Breeding Plans, Jay L. Lush: Iowa State University Press, Ames, Iowa, 1945.

Animal Management, prepared in the Veterinary Department of the War Office, Her Majesty's Stationery Office, London, 1933.

Animal Nutrition, Leonard A. Maynard and John K. Loosli: McGraw-Hill Book Company, Inc., New York, 1962.

Animal Sanitation and Disease Control, R. R. Dykstra: The Interstate Printers & Publishers, Inc., Danville, Illinois, 1955

Applied Animal Nutrition, E. W. Crampton: W. H. Freeman and Company, San Francisco, 1956.

Better Pastures for Horses and Ponies, Robert W. Duell: Extension Bulletin 350-A, Rutgers—The State University, New Brunswick, New Jersey, 1964.

Breeding Better Livestock, Victor Arthur Rice, Frederick N. Andrews, and Everett J. Warwick: McGraw-Hill Book Company, Inc., New York, 1953.

Cavalcade of American Horses, Pers Crowell: McGraw-Hill Book Company, Inc., New York, 1951.

The Complete Book of the Quarter Horse, Nelson C. Nye: A. S. Barnes and Co., Inc., New York, 1964.

Equine Medicine and Surgery, American Veterinary Publications, Inc., Wheaton, Illinois, 1963.

External Parasites of Horses, J. O. Rowell: Leaflet 195, Virginia Polytechnic Institute, Blacksburg, Virginia, 1966.

Feeding Horses and Ponies, Byron E. Colby: Special Circular 284, University of Massachusetts, Amherst, Massachusetts, 1964.

Feeding Light Horses and Ponies, A. N. Huff: Circular 969, Virginia Polytechnic Institute, Blacksburg, Virginia, 1965.

Feeds and Feeding, Frank B. Morrison: The Morrison Publishing Company, Ithaca, New York, 1957.

"First Aid," William E. Eggert: *The Blood Horse*, Vol. XC, No. 9, Page 2052, 1965.

4-H Horse Club Handbook for Members, 4-H 83, Rutgers—The State University, New Brunswick, New Jersey, 1963.

4-H Horse Program Leaders' Guide, National 4-H Service Committee, Inc., Chicago, Illinois, 1965.

Fundamentals of Nutrition, E. W. Crampton and L. E. Lloyd: W. H. Freeman and Company, San Francisco, 1959.

Genetics of Livestock Improvement, John F. Lasley: Prentice-Hall, Inc., Englewood Cliffs, New Jersey, 1963.

Grooming Horses, R. W. Collins: *The Blood Horse*, Lexington, Kentucky, 1959.

The Horse, D. J. Kays: Rinehart & Company, Inc., New York, 1953.

"The Horse and Our Nation's Economy," California State Horsemen's Association, *Western Horseman*, Vol. XXIX, No. 5, Page 64, 1964.

Horse Judging Guide, Frederick Harper, 4-H 82, Rutgers—The State University, New Brunswick, New Jersey, 1964.

"Horse Nutrition and Feeding," T. J. Cunha, *Feedstuffs*, Vol. 35, Nos. 35, 36; p. 18, 1963.

The Horse Parasites, Douglas N. Stern, Byron Colby and Ellsworth Wheeler, Publication 418, University of Massachusetts, Amherst, Massachusetts, 1964.

Horse Science (4-H Horse Program), National 4-H Service Committee, Inc., Chicago, Illinois, 1965.

Horse Science Handbook, from the Horse Science School, M. E. Ensminger, Director 1963, 1964.

Horse Sense About Hay, W. H. Mitchell, E. N. Scarborough and W. T. McAllister: Extension Bulletin 78, University of Delaware, Newark, Delaware, 1962.

A Horseman's Handbook on Practical Breeding, Col. John F. Wall: Washington Planograph Company, Inc., Washington, D.C. (Published by Thoroughbred Bloodlines, Camden, South Carolina), 1950.

Horsemastership, Margaret Cabell Self: A. S. Barnes and Co., Inc., New York, 1952.

Horses and Horsemanship (4-H Horse Program), National 4-H Service Committee, Inc., Chicago, Illinois, 1965.

Horses and Horsemanship, M. E. Ensminger: The Interstate Printers & Publishers, Inc., Danville, Illinois, 1963.

Horses Need High Quality Hay, Forage for Vitamin A, G. W. VanderNoot, P. V. Fonnesbeck and C. L. Garton: New Jersey Agriculture, Vol. 47, No. 2, 1965.

Insect Pests of Livestock in North Carolina, W. G. Bruce: Extension Circular 456, North Carolina State University, Raleigh, North Carolina, 1965.

Livestock Pest Control, C. K. Dorsey, H. E. Kidder, C. J. Cunningham and C. B. Boyles: Circular 113, West Virginia University, Morgantown, West Virginia, 1964.

Losses in Agriculture, U.S.D.A., Agriculture Handbook No. 291, August, 1965.

The Manual of Horsemanship of the British Horse Society and the Pony Club, The British Horse Society, London (W. E. Baxter, Ltd., Sussex, printers), 1964 (1st printing 1950).

The Merck Veterinary Manual, O. H. Siegmund, Ed.: Merck & Company, Inc., Rahway, New Jersey, 1961.

Modern Breeds of Livestock, Hilton M. Briggs: The Macmillan Company, New York, 1958.

New Jersey Equine Survey, Circular 421, New Jersey Department of Agriculture, Trenton, New Jersey, 1961.

New York Equine Survey, Harold A. Willman: Animal Husbandry Mimeo, Series 2, Cornell University, Ithaca, New York, 1965.

Nutrient Requirements of the Light Horse, Albert Wendell Nelson: American Quarter Horse Association, Amarillo, Texas, 1961.

The Physiology of Domestic Animals, H. H. Dukes, D.V.M.: Comstock Publishing Associates, Ithaca, New York, 1955.

Practical Animal Husbandry, William C. Miller and E. D. S. Robertson: Oliver and Boyd, London, 1959.

Preference of Various Baled and Pelleted Hay Mixtures by Horses, William H. Mitchell and John H. Shropshire: Misc. Paper 343, University of Delaware, Newark, Delaware.

Proceedings of the Horse Training and Management Short Course, MP-528, Texas A & M University, College Station, Texas, 1961.

Proceedings of the Horse Management and Training Short Course, MP-587, Texas A & M University, College Station, Texas, 1962.

Proceedings of the Horse Short Course, MP-697, Texas A & M University, College Station, Texas, 1964.

Productive Horse Husbandry, Carl W. Gay, D.V.M.: J. B. Lippincott Co., Philadelphia, 1932.

The Quarter Horse As I See Him, Bob Sutherland: Kansas City, Missouri, 1953.

Recommended Nutrients Allowances for Horses, National Research Council, Washington, D.C., 1949.

Reproduction in Farm Animals, E. S. E. Hafez: Lea & Febiger, Philadelphia, 1962.

Reproductive Physiology, A. V. Nalbandov: W. H. Freeman and Company, San Francisco, 1958.

Social Behavior of Horses, Wally McLane: paper for seminar, Montana State College, Bozeman, Montana, 1965.

The Stockman's Handbook, M. E. Ensminger: The Interstate Printers & Publishers, Inc., Danville, Illinois, 1962.

Stud Managers' Handbook, from the Stud Managers' Course, Washington State University, Pullman, Washington, 1961.

Stud Managers' Handbook, Vol. 1, from the Stud Managers' School, Phoenix, Arizona, M. E. Ensminger, Director, 1965.

A Study of Growth and Development in the Quarter Horse, Kirby Cunningham and Stewart H. Fowler: Bulletin 546, Louisiana State University, Baton Rouge, 1961.

"Utilization of the Carotene of Hay by Horses," Paul V. Fonnesbeck, George W. VanderNoot and Linda D. Symons: *Journal Animal Science,* Vol. XXV, No. 3, Page 891, 1966 (abstract).

Veterinary Anatomy, Robert Getty: Burgess Publishing Co., Minneapolis 15, Minnesota, 1953.

Veterinary Notebook, William R. McGee, D.V.M.: *The Blood Horse,* Lexington, Kentucky, 1958.

"Vitamin A in Horse Nutrition," Paul V. Fonnesbeck: *Animal Nutrition and Health,* Vol. XXI, No. 8, Page 9, 1966.

"Vitamin E for Muscle Development," Howard D. Stowe: *The Blood Horse,* Vol. XCI, No. 3, Page 164, 1966.

Index

Index